DEAFNESS, CHILDREN AND THE FAMILY

For my mother, and in memory of my father

Deafness, Children and the Family

A Guide to Professional Practice

Dr Jennifer Densham
University of Hertfordshire

Published by
Arena
Ashgate Publishing Limited
Gower House
Croft Road
Aldershot
Hants GU11 3HR
England

Ashgate Publishing Company
Old Post Road
Brookfield
Vermont 05036
USA

British Library Cataloguing in Publication Data

Densham, Jennifer
    Deafness, Children and the Family:
    Guide to Professional Practice
    I. Title
    362.420 83
    ISBN 1-85742-221-X

Library of Congress Cataloging-in-Publication Data

Densham, Jennifer, 1949–
    Deafness, children and the family:
    a guide to professional practice/
    Jennifer Densham.
        p.   cm.
    Includes bibliographical references (p.   ).
    ISBN 1-85742-221-X: £25.00 ($46.95 US: est.)
    1. Social work with the deaf. 2. Children, Deaf.
    3. Parents of handicapped children.
    I. Title.
    HV2391.D46 1995   94–34122
    362.7–dc20   CIP

Typeset by Bournemouth Colour Graphics, Parkstone, Dorset and printed in Great Britain by Biddles Limited, Guildford

Contents

List of figures

Acknowledgements

I am indebted to many people, friends, colleagues and others who have participated in the creation of this book, including members of the general public, parents (of deaf and hearing children), school children and staff, teachers of the deaf, health visitors, library and computer staff, and others too numerous to mention each by name.

I would like to express my appreciation in particular to: Mrs Pearl Batten, Pam Bradbury, Carol Couch, Chris Cox, Samantha Densham-Potts, Melita Gibson, Alan Hanslow, Dr Gareth Holsgrove, Velda and Clive Jenkinson, Dr Kandiah, Pam Kent, Harry Kernohan, Rikki Kittel, Sally Knight, Teresa and Rawden Lau, Jo-Ann Lynch, Wendy Mears, Margit Rodgers, Keith Scott, David Scott, Gillian Smith, Robert Taylor and Dr Andy Wroot.

Finally, I would especially like to thank Gabriel Newfield, Dr Kenneth MacKinnon, Jo Campling, Mary McClymont, Joanna Brady, Michael Hunt, Dr Michael Taylor, Rosemary Taylor and Anita and Andrew Chu for their support and practical help.

Introduction

This is a research-based book intended for professionals in medical, educational, health and social work fields who come into contact with deaf children and their families. Many of the issues raised also have implications for professionals working with parents of children with other forms of disability.

In terms of the general population in the United Kingdom, severe and profound deafness is relatively rare. For this reason, when a diagnosis of deafness is made, few parents have either the knowledge or experience to question professional decisions regarding their child. Power and control are readily relinquished to 'the experts', yet decisions made – in particular around the time of diagnosis – may have far-reaching consequences in terms of social and emotional development and the eventual life outcomes for the child. Important decisions (especially concerning communication and education) are often made when parents are still in a state of shock, coming to terms with the realization that their child has a serious and permanent disability.

For the majority of deaf parents, the diagnosis of deafness in their child tends not to have such an emotionally traumatic impact as it does for hearing parents. In order to communicate with a profoundly deaf child, hearing parents may need to learn a foreign language (usually British Sign Language in the UK), whereas for those deaf parents who already use sign language, communication is not a problem. Also, with hearing parents there may be an inability to identify with a child who is different from them, whereas for deaf parents their child is not different, so this difficulty does not arise. Throughout the book, discussion about parental reactions relates to those of hearing parents.

The book has an eclectic perspective, drawing information from a range of disciplines (psychology, sociology, anthropology, education, biology, etc.), and throughout the work, where relevant, further reading is indicated in the notes at the end of chapters. This is intended mainly for students, but may also prove useful for professionals whose expertise is drawn mainly from a single discipline.

Many variables affect the social development of deaf children, including family dynamics, their language development and the mode of communication used, the kind of education they receive, and their eventual integration into the wider normal-hearing society. No single area can be viewed in isolation as each has an interactive effect on all the others, and each is addressed in this book. However, for convenience, they are set out as discrete chapters.

Part II has been included for the reader who is unfamiliar with the anatomical and physiological aspects of deafness. It is a very brief overview, and the reader is directed towards further reading for more detailed information.

A large number of people were interviewed for the study, and names, where used, have been changed to protect their identity.

This book illustrates the need for change in some professional practice, and focuses attention on those areas where change may be effected. The attitudes of professionals have been found to have a marked effect on the attitudes and behaviour of parents, which in turn affects the way they react to their children. Parents must feel good about themselves in order to foster a sense of confidence in their deaf children. Unresolved negative feelings can affect their childrearing abilities, sometimes with disastrous consequences. Three areas are highlighted where professional involvement can have a profound effect on the socialization of deaf children: diagnosis, communication and education.

It is intended that, by raising awareness of the issues involved, professionals may gain greater understanding and insight, so enabling them to become more sensitive to the needs of deaf children and their families. Also, by examining their own practice and interaction with families, beneficial changes may be made where necessary, so that, as deaf children grow up, a positive self-image is developed, and their self-esteem enhanced.

Part I

1　The impact of deafness

I was at boarding school from 6 until 16 years. When I left school it was a different world. I cried every night. I didn't know how to interact with hearing people. I didn't know the facts of life. I could only communicate on a two-word level – 'How are you? Well, thank you.' I had no communication and I felt very lonely.

It was a problem for the other kids – for the little ones. The hearing aids he had to wear – they used to frighten the other little ones. One little boy who lived round the corner, he was scared stiff of John. Used to run away from him down the street.

He's only 2. He doesn't understand why his toys don't make a noise any more.

The impact of diagnosis

In the UK, 90 per cent of deaf children are born to hearing parents (Kyle and Woll 1988). For the majority of these parents the discovery that their child is deaf comes as a devastating shock. In contrast, deaf parents do not tend to experience the diagnosis of deafness in their child as the same kind of disaster, particularly if the household communicates in sign language (Grant 1987; Schlesinger 1985). For this reason, concerns surrounding the impact of the diagnosis and parental reactions discussed in this chapter and later in the book focus on those found among hearing parents.

The birth of a baby is a profound and deeply moving experience for most parents, and the discovery – or even the suspicion – that a new infant is not perfect can be shattering (Powell et al 1985). If there has been some abnormality surrounding the birth (for example, prematurity or birth trauma), or an obvious cause such as maternal rubella or meningitis in the child, parents may have some preparation for the possibility of there being something wrong with their child. Even so, any abnormality, no matter how apparently insignificant to others, can cause distress, and parents may take a long time to come to terms with such a potentially serious diagnosis of deafness. Because of complicating factors such as delays in getting appointments (Schlesinger and Meadow 1972; Densham 1990), and disappointing results of hearing screening (Bellman 1987; Martin and Moore 1979; Martin et al 1981; Newton 1985) as well as difficulties in diagnosing the level of loss in young infants, parents may remain in a state of anxiety about the degree of impairment their child possesses for a prolonged period of time (Graham 1986; Ross 1990; Schlesinger and Meadow 1972). Therefore professionals have a vital role to play during this period.

Whether a child is born deaf or becomes deaf, no matter how well hearing parents may eventually come to accept the diagnosis, initially there will always be a crisis to overcome. Help and support will be needed in coming to terms with the permanency of the condition and the long-term implications.

How parents feel about, and act towards, their children will affect the way those children come to view themselves, and may have long-lasting effects on later social relationships as well as career decisions, future lifestyles, etc., possibly throughout life.

The time of diagnosis is perhaps the most critical period, when decisions are made which can have far-reaching consequences for the rest of a child's life. It is a time when professionals need to be at their most sensitive to the needs and feelings of the family. How the diagnosis is imparted to parents, and the subsequent follow-up care, has a profound significance for the way parents come to view their children and react towards them.

A study by Woolley et al (1989) on imparting the diagnosis of life-threatening illness found that clear patterns emerged concerning which elements of the discussion parents appreciated or resented. They found that all parents remembered vividly the manner in which the diagnosis was imparted, and that some parents were still preoccupied with this many years later.

Although the diagnosis of deafness is less serious than diagnosis of a life-threatening illness, similar reactions were found among the parents who were interviewed in this study (see also Meadow 1980). For example, the father of a profoundly deaf 9-year-old boy had tears in his eyes as he related his memories of being given the diagnosis:

> It was eight years ago nearly. It never leaves you – never leaves your mind. They don't prepare people beforehand. It was so cold . . . just . . . a miserable sort of place really. Just me and me wife and John and there was nobody else, nobody else in this backwater of a place. It didn't seem as if we was going somewhere that you'd expect to go to . . . to be told that sort of stuff that you just was hope ... hopefully thinking might not be. It just seemed . . . sort of like a backwater type place to be told really bad news.

We never seen anybody else. There was only the doctor there and I think the receptionist type or a nurse. If I could have chosen how to have been told it would have been a bit more – bit more important. To be given to you not solemnly but not frivolous: 'He's deaf – nothing we can do.' It was as if I was supposed to know. Told it was nerve loss. I didn't know. That doctor . . . told you as if you should just understand it straightaway and be cool like. I had to take it back – I didn't understand . . . I asked if they might be able to do an operation. 'Oh no. He's deaf and that's the end.' We come out.

If we'd been told 'You're going to have a problem. You need to come to terms with it.' But not all cold like that.

It is well known that parents go through a process of grieving the loss of a 'perfect' child in order to be able to accept a 'new' child with a disability, and this process has been well documented (for example, Buscaglia 1975; Gordon 1975; Kubler-Ross 1969; Moses 1977, 1985; Murray-Parkes 1975; Stewart 1978; Webster 1976). The stages of grief include denial, guilt, depression, anger and anxiety, before acceptance.

Moses (1985) has specifically set out the grieving process as it relates to parents whose child is diagnosed as deaf, stressing the importance of early psychosocial intervention in order to help parents work through the process effectively. He reminds us that disability in a child shatters cherished and significant dreams (which require an unimpaired child), and that it is the *dream* that must be grieved for. Because this is such a personal and illusory loss, few people understand that it is a dream that has been lost, and they are therefore frequently confused by the grief process that follows. Also, successful grieving seems to depend on significant human interactions, yet those wishing to offer support may fail to recognize that each of the affective states in the grieving process serves a specific function that allows the parents to separate from the cherished dream.

Parental reactions during the grieving process (particularly the expression of negative feelings such as anger or rage) may affect professional workers, especially if they do not understand the process and its importance. Sometimes adverse relationships between parents and professionals can result (Powell et al. 1985).

According to Moses (1985):

Professionals who have negative opinions or difficulty with the affective states . . . are likely to inhibit the grief process and be detrimental to the habilitation of the child. The professional who is able to convey an attitude of acceptance toward the affective states will have a positive effect upon the parents and help to create a sense of security for the child. Without this, children cannot go on to develop in other areas, such as language development, that are seen as tantamount to the successful habilitation of a deaf child. (p.99)

Meadow (1980) has also argued that, until parents have the opportunity to examine their feelings and to express anger, guilt and sorrow, these negative feelings can interfere with the parents' relationship with their child, and reduce the energy and coping strengths necessary to overcome the consequences of deafness; and that 'there are some families who continue to relive the diagnostic trauma throughout the life of the child' (p.134).

For the first few months of life the relationship between parents and a deaf child is typically normal (Altschuler 1974; Lenneberg 1967; Schlesinger and Meadow 1972; Harris 1978) but by the second half of the first year parental expectations are not met. The child's behaviour deviates increasingly from what is considered to be normal. When a child fails to turn in response to sound, parents may feel rejected or deprived, and this is the beginning of an interruption in parent–child interaction (Harris 1978).

Many authors (for example, Graham 1986; Harris 1978; Altschuler 1974; Schlesinger and Meadow 1972; Luterman 1979) have pointed out that parental suspicion that there is something wrong with their child often precedes diagnosis by several months, and this intervening period is one of uncertainty and anxiety for the family, hence reactions to the initial diagnosis can vary considerably.

Initially many parents may feel relief at finally receiving confirmation of a diagnosis (Woolley et al 1989; Luterman 1979). In the present study some of the parents of deaf children responded to the diagnosis with initial feelings of relief. For example:

> I was relieved because I knew there was something wrong with him and no one would listen to me.

> I was just relieved that at last I'd been proved right. I knew he wasn't hearing me.

On the other hand, the diagnosis can be devastating. On hearing that her child had a sensorineural hearing loss, another mother reported:

> I was staggered. Didn't expect it. Wouldn't believe it was permanent. I was just told that she had a permanent hearing loss. No other information. I just felt stunned.

Schlesinger and Meadow (1972) found that, during the process of diagnosis, when hearing parents were sent from one doctor to another, they often became increasingly anxious and frustrated. Frequently medical experts accused them of being over-anxious, inadequate or incompetent. Similar findings came from parents interviewed during the course of the research for this book. For example, the mother of a 3-year-old boy with a hearing impairment explained:

> I actually asked for him to have a hearing test in the January of last year – so it was before he was 2. I actually got it in August. They kept saying 'It'll be through in six

weeks, it'll be through in six weeks' and I had to keep going down every six weeks and it took from January until August to get it.

I suspected there was something wrong. I had to talk to him face to face. If I was behind him he couldn't hear me. When he was finally diagnosed I was relieved. I think because I'm a single parent I was sort of classed as an over-anxious mother. I'd been down there before with having his eyes tested ... Basically I just felt that because I'd gone down there before and insisted on having things done that they thought 'Oh she's going to bother us again. Oh what's she come in for this time'... as far as they were concerned I was worrying over nothing. I was getting brushed off. An over-anxious parent.

The child in the following example was not diagnosed as profoundly deaf until $2^1/_2$ years of age, despite an original referral at 3 months by the GP, and a further referral following the 7-month hearing screening test:

I felt really angry. You listen to the doctor and do what you're told. She was always ill. It was as though they didn't believe me. They put me down as a neurotic mother. A mother knows when there's something wrong. She's with the child 24 hours a day.

I had a very good GP and health visitor – no complaints there. Only with the hospital. When we got to the other hospital ... she was operated on within two weeks. They took one look and said 'This is an emergency.'

In a further example, a mother with a profoundly deaf son (now an adult) spent five years 'fighting' doctors to have his hearing tested. He was misdiagnosed as being educationally subnormal (ESN), and requests by his mother for hearing tests were repeatedly refused. The child was 5 years and 8 months of age before a diagnosis of profound hearing loss was made. The label of ESN remained throughout his school days (his mother presumes that this was because he also had cerebral palsy). He was not educated by teachers of the deaf, and he learned neither speech nor sign language. At interview this mother relived some of the frustration she had felt over thirty years previously in trying to get a professional to listen to her. Eventually she became so angry that the family doctor took notice and referred her child to an audiological clinic, against the wishes of the paediatrician whose clinic he was attending.

This case highlights two problems, a lack of acceptance of parental anxiety, and interprofessional jealousy and role confusion.

Tweedie (1987) has argued that parents of deaf children should not be dismissed with words of comfort: the words of comfort are appropriate, but not the dismissal; and that, if a parent suspects a hearing problem, it must be pursued until a reliable result is obtained, although 'there is little value in detecting a large number of children with problems if no back up service is available to refer them to' (p.vi).

The manner in which grief is experienced and responded to by others may be important in determining whether that grief is benign or harmful (Fulton and Gottesman 1980). Many professionals who would be in a good position to support parents through the grieving process are unable to do so, either because of a lack of understanding of the purpose of each phase (so that each is seen as negative and something to be discouraged), or because of the dilemma of reconciling intervention with the parents' need to deny the hearing loss (Moses 1985; Freeman et al 1981). The grieving process may also be affected by other factors, such as a lack of time or resources.

The diagnosis of hearing loss puts tremendous pressures and burdens on the family in terms of energy, time and money, as well as in terms of the audiological and educational needs of the child; and parents are often besieged from all sides by professionals giving new skills advice and information (Luterman 1979; Meadow 1980). (See Figure 1.1.)

It has been found by Luterman that, as parents begin to acknowledge the awfulness of the situation, they feel emotionally overwhelmed and inadequate. Without background knowledge they are unable to judge the quality of information given by professionals, relations or friends; and often they are given too much information in too short a space of time. (Perhaps those who have experienced first-time parenthood will have some idea of how confusing it can be to receive possibly conflicting advice from all directions.)

According to Harris (1978) the mother may suffer a reactive depression following diagnosis, thus interrupting important processes in the child's development (because of an inability to respond to the needs of the child), and leading to emotional and cognitive problems that do not yield to later intervention.

Schlesinger (1976, 1985) has argued that a lack of support by professionals during the diagnostic crisis, followed by professional advice that is seen as overwhelming, conflicting and incompatible, can contribute to stress, and often lead to a crisis in parenting. (Research evidence has shown that parents of deaf children tend to be more controlling and intrusive than parents of hearing children: for example, Brinich 1980; Greenberg 1980; Schlesinger and Meadow 1972). The child evokes a sense of powerlessness, which in turn evokes control, and mental health may suffer as a consequence (see also Levitt and Cohen 1977). Self-esteem is a crucial component of mental health, and problems with low self-esteem often characterize deaf children and their parents (see also Chapter 6).

Evidence from the research for this book suggests that a sense of powerlessness may also be evoked in the parents by the professionals with whom they have initial contact (see Chapter 7).

Professionals have a responsibility to parents and their children. The impact of deafness on hearing parents can affect the whole life outcomes of their children, embracing their self-esteem, ability to communicate, their

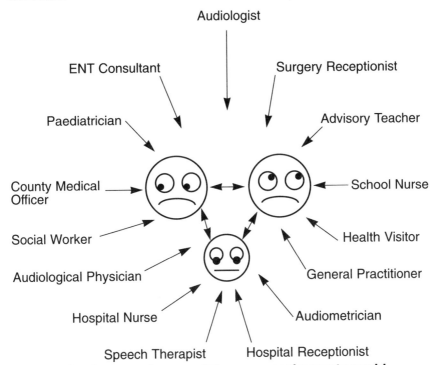

Figure 1.1 **A range of some of the personnel parents could encounter following diagnosis of hearing impairment in their child**

education and integration into society. By their attitudes professionals influence parents, who influence their children. In turn those children become adults and influence future generations, and so a dynamic process is set up which has begun with the professional. Therefore, insightful and caring professionals can have a profound and positive effect on this whole interactive cycle.

2 Theories and concepts of development

Introduction

In this chapter consideration is given to the range of theories of child development and schools of thought from which the concept of socialization has emerged, and how the concept is changing from that of a 'given' state to an ongoing dynamic process, in the light of new technology and methods of studying interactive processes.

Socialization is central to the understanding of behaviour in general, but is particularly important when considering people with hearing impairment in a hearing society because of the implications for the person who is not 'socialized' to fit into that society. Such persons (whether deaf or hearing) are perceived as 'different' from the rest of the group and are given labels accordingly: for example, 'deviant', 'maladjusted', 'mentally ill', 'emotionally disturbed', 'behavioural problem', etc. (Goffman 1973, 1976). Deaf people, by the very nature of their impairment, tend to be seen as different from the majority and are therefore at greater risk of labelling and stigmatization (see Chapter 6).

Attitudes towards children, and consequent actions and reactions to them during the formative years, may set a pattern which can affect the whole of a child's life. For example, given adverse conditions a 'difficult' baby may develop into a 'problem' child, then a 'juvenile delinquent' and finally a 'hardened criminal' (although the words used to label people may change with the fashion, the concepts behind them tend to remain fairly constant). Once a person has been perceived in a certain way, people may behave towards that person in such a way as to provoke the expected response (Goffman 1973). In this way patterns of behaviour may become fixed in childhood. There are also many recorded cases where, despite incredibly adverse conditions, children manage to develop into 'socialized' beings

9

within their own cultural group (for example, see Doyle 1988).

'Society' feels that it has a duty to protect and deter, and thus the consequence for a person who does not fit in generally tends towards some form of ostracism (for example, prison, mental institution, residential care for children, etc.) or some other form of control (for example, drugs to control behaviour, probation, electronic tagging, or some form of avoidance). This in turn may lead to isolation, loneliness, frustration, depression or aggression on the part of the ostracized person.

Definitions and theoretical perspectives

'"Socialization" is the term used to describe the means by which children learn the rules, values, forms of behaviour and culture of the society into which they are born. It is the process of learning the behaviour patterns that enable people to interact meaningfully, organized by adults in order that successive generations shall learn the blueprint for living that we call "culture"' (Shipman 1972).

In turn, 'culture', as defined by Linton (1947), is 'the configuration of learned behaviour and results of behaviour whose component elements are shared and transmitted to members of a particular society' (p.21). It refers to the total way of life of any society, but does not include instinctive behaviour or basic needs and tensions, although these obviously have some influence on culture (for example, eating is a response to the need for nourishment, but the way we eat depends on how we have learned to eat).

Argyle (1976) also considered the culture of a group to be their whole way of life, arguing that language, ways of perceiving, categorizing and thinking about the world, forms of non-verbal communication and social interaction, rules and conventions about behaviour, moral values and ideals, technology and material culture, art, science, literature and history are all aspects which affect social behaviour either directly or indirectly (p.139).

Many authors from varying social science backgrounds have argued that the fundamental mechanism of socialization is a process of interacting and identifying with others; and that the patterns of interaction imposed are highly relative and vary from culture to culture (for example, Bandura 1969; Berger and Berger 1978; Danziger 1978; Farb 1977; Kellmer Pringle 1966; Kerckhoff 1972; McCandless 1969; McNeil 1969; Rheingold 1969; Schaffer and Crook 1978; Zigler and Child 1973).

This has important relevance when considering the concept of deaf culture and the deaf community. A child brought up in a hearing family environment has very different experience from a child developing within a deaf cultural setting. In some cases, this can lead to difficulties of acceptance from an alien cultural group later in life (see Chapter 5).

The study of the process of socialization forms large areas of anthropology, psychology and sociology, and the term was first used in its modern sense almost simultaneously (in 1939 and 1940) by independent scholars in all three disciplines (Hargreaves 1985; Danziger 1978). How children learn and incorporate the values and ideologies of their particular cultural group has been studied from a range of different perspectives over many years, yet, to date, the actual process of socialization is not fully understood.

Historically, the psychological forms of the concept developed from the work of Binet and Simon on measuring intelligence, which led to the long-argued debates over geneticism versus environmentalism, and had an effect on shaping the schools of thought currently in existence today (Burton 1972). McDougall (1908) studied social development and incorporated a long list of instincts into his theory, suggesting that the child responded to outside influences as does an animal, while Baldwin (1897) considered that children have an innate inclination to imitate, which occurs in specific stages of development. In order to be able to imitate, there must be outside influences, which suggested that the environment is primarily responsible for how a child is socialized.

According to Hargreaves (1985), the 'culture personality' school tried to draw together the approaches of different disciplines by applying psychoanalytic theory to anthropological data, but the effort failed, probably due to the overwhelming scale and interdisciplinary nature of the task; current studies tend to be intra- rather than interdisciplinary.

Over the years a range of perspectives have developed, including behaviourism, symbolic interactionism, psychoanalysis, social-learning theory, cognitive development, social phenomenology and field theory, all of which contribute to a greater understanding of the process of socialization, which is discussed later in this chapter.

Behaviourism

In 1919 Watson proposed that a person's actions (apart from a limited number of innate reflexes) were completely the product of conditioning experiences (Burton 1972). At this time, this was construed as the complete opposite of the instinct assumptions, whereas today this position has been modified somewhat. Watson demanded that only external events and directly observable behaviour be considered in building a theory. Although the influence of his own theory declined after a decade, the attitude towards scientific investigations of behaviour through experimental methods has been lasting, and it is only comparatively recently that alternative methods of investigating social behaviour have begun to take on greater importance. For example, Schaffer (1986) argues that laboratory demonstration models do not show that something which can be done in a laboratory is necessarily the way it happens in real life (see also Dunn and Kendrick 1979; White 1977; Danziger 1978).

B.F. Skinner further developed Watson's work on behaviourism. He argued that meaning is given to a situation by a process of internalized reinforcement: that is, the internal feeling associated with reinforcement is perceived as 'good', so the individual behaves in a way that will reinforce that feeling. Skinner was only concerned with phenomena that he claimed were observable, measurable and experimentally manipulable (Skinner 1974; see also Skinner 1953, 1957).

Symbolic interactionism

George Herbert Mead (1934), who laid the foundations of the symbolic interactionist approach, was influenced by Watson (Blumer 1969). Mead considered that the self is essentially a social construction which arises out of social experience. The infant has no character or personality when born, but takes on the attitudes of others by role-playing, and so comes to assimilate the morale of the larger community of which he is a part.

Mead went beyond the behaviourist approach and argued that people are not simply the outcome of their social environment, but that human beings give meaning to their world. As a person develops he becomes aware of himself as himself, 'I', and himself in relation to others, 'me' (the me that I can see), through taking on different roles in the socialization process. He also develops a sense of 'other' (both 'significant other', which stems from the key people in his life, such as parents, siblings, etc., and the 'generalized other', that is, society as a whole) and learns to act in accordance with these images. This is a continuing process throughout life, which means that a person's behaviour can change at any time.

Freudian psychoanalysis

Freudian psychoanalysis began as a study of neurosis and as a hypothesis explaining its origin and development (Lomas 1968). Lomas cites Home (1966), who argued that Freud adopted a totally new principle of explanation which ran counter to the tenor of thought prevalent in medicine at that time – that a symptom could have meaning. This eventually led him on to formulate his revolutionary ideas about the unconscious mind. In discovering that the symptom had meaning, and basing his treatment on this hypothesis, Freud took the psychoanalytic study of neurosis out of the world of science into the world of humanities; and, as Home points out, 'the logic and method of humanities is radically different from that of science, though no less respectable and rational and of course much longer established'

(Home 1966, p.117).

In contrast to the symbolic interactionist approach, and that of the behaviourists, the Freudian psychoanalytic school was concerned with the inner perspectives of the self as a being from birth, and how the infant makes sense of, and relates and adapts to, outside forces by the use of psychological defence mechanisms. Freud was looking for unconscious motives that direct behaviour, and he believed that repressed sexual and aggressive impulses generated anxiety within the individual. He suggested that there are unconscious processes that defend a person against anxiety by distorting reality in some way. For example, a common immediate reaction on being given bad news is denial; or a traumatic incident which is too threatening to remember may be blocked from conscious awareness by the use of repression. (This is different from suppression, where the individual consciously holds down a feeling or memory. With suppression there is deliberate self-control, whereas with repression the person is unaware that they have the feeling.)

Freud saw personality as composed of three major systems: the id, the ego and the superego. Each of these systems has its own function, but the three interact to govern behaviour.

The id is the original source of personality, present from birth, from which the ego and superego develop later. It is unconscious and consists of everything that is inherited, including the instinctual drives (sex and aggression). The id is closely linked to the biological processes and provides the energy source for operating all three systems. It works on the pleasure principle and seeks immediate gratification, endeavouring to avoid pain and obtain pleasure, regardless of any external considerations.

The superego is the conscience – the part that represents the values and morals that are taught to the child by parents and others. It judges whether actions are right or wrong, and punishes by making a person feel guilty, or rewards by making them feel proud.

The ego works on the reality principle, and may delay gratification until the appropriate time. It acts as a mediator between the demands of the id, the realities of the world, and the demands of the superego.[1]

Freud argued that children pass through a series of stages as they develop. Each stage focuses on a particular area of the body and its associated activities (these are the oral, anal, phallic or oedipal stages, latency, and finally the genital stage). Unresolved conflicts at any of these stages can result in a person becoming stuck, or fixated, may prevent mature personality development, and could lead to mental illness.

For Freud, the first initial influences on the growing child come from the family, and he emphasized how early childhood experiences can affect personality development. Meanings are fixed in childhood and are extremely resistant to change in later life – whereas with symbolic interactionism, meanings are changing all the time.[2]

Social-learning theory

According to Hargreaves (1985, p.775), early attempts in psychology by the neobehaviourists (for example, R. Sears, N. Miller, J. Dollard and A. Bandura) to explain human behaviour in terms of conditioned responses to environmental stimuli, learned by association with rewards and punishments, ran into severe problems. They realized that it was not possible to explain the full complexity of human behaviour in terms of simple learning processes, so concepts such as 'internalization' and 'identification' were introduced. This modified form of reinforcement theory became known as social-learning theory (see, for example, Bandura and Walters 1963; Bandura 1969).

Social-learning theory focuses on patterns of behaviour that are learned in coping with the environment, either directly or through observing the consequences of behaviour modelled by another person. This paradigm considers that reinforcement comes through the identification and imitation of the reinforced model; that is, the child internalizes the concept 'I am good' through identification with significant people in the child's life.

As with the symbolic interactionist approach, social-learning theory suggests that behaviour can be changed at any time. Abnormal or maladaptive behaviour is seen as the result of faulty learning during the course of growing up (Bandura 1977) and can be altered either by changing the environment or by promoting the learning of new behaviour.

Cognitive developmental theory

Cognitive developmental theory was developed by Piaget during the 1920s–1930s, but in recent years there has been a revival of interest in his approach (Hargreaves 1985, p.776). For Piaget, the child constructs his own meaning of the world through interaction with others and his own exploration. Piaget suggests that there are definite stages of orderly progression through which a child passes, each happening in a sequence so that one stage must be completed before the next one is reached. This suggests that the child has inherited developmental tendencies, which has similarities with the psychoanalytic view. According to Bernal (1974), for Piaget the mother is important because she is the most central source of reciprocal exchange. She is normally the most available and most responsive person to the child, and therefore acts as a means for him or her to explore and develop, whereas from the Freudian viewpoint the mother (or main carer) is the most important figure in shaping the child's personality. (For further reading the reader is referred to Piaget 1932, 1951, 1953, 1968, 1971.)

Social phenomenology

Social phenomenological theory, which is concerned with how each individual creates his or her own reality compared to the reality of others, was developed by Alfred Schutz during the 1930s. According to Wagner (1975), prior to the work of Schutz, three studies – by Bergson (1938), James (1890) and Husserl (1928) – eventually gained equal importance for the development of a phenomenological approach to the field of sociology. Wagner argued that the later writings of Schutz (for example, Schutz 1932) constitute the framework of a sociology based on phenomenological considerations, and that the work of Husserl and of Weber (1922a, 1922b) formed the cornerstone of his thinking.

This approach seeks to understand events or 'phenomena' as they are experienced by the individual, without imposing any preconceptions or theoretical ideas. The concern is with reality as it is perceived by the individual. This theory suggests that people are not acted on by forces outside their control, but that individuals are capable of controlling their own destiny.

The concept of socialization, although generally embraced within the framework developed by Schutz, was not directly addressed by him. Social phenomenological theory has been further developed and applied to the study of socialization by such authors as Berger and Luckman (1967), who argued that, although a child comes to make sense of the world through interaction with other people, defining and measuring reality remains a highly subjective process.

Field theory

Kurt Lewin developed the concept of field theory during the 1930s and 1940s as a way of explaining psychological events, and claimed that it is best characterized as a method of analysing causal relations and of building scientific constructs (Lewin 1952). Lewin argued that behaviour is related to forces which are acting on a person at that time, and he constructed a system of tension to represent psychological needs. For Lewin, 'tension' refers to the state of one system relative to the state of surrounding systems, and there is a tendency for change in the direction of equalization of the state of neighbouring systems (p.11). He argued that, instead of drawing out isolated incidents when trying to understand behaviour, field theory takes into consideration the situation as a whole. According to Burton (1972) and Deutsch (1972), field theory is a conceptual scheme which derives from the gestalt principle of considering the total situation – all the factors in the environment which might influence behaviour, as well as the personality characteristics of the individual. From this perspective the whole is seen as more than the sum of its parts. In the same way that a clock is made up of mechanical pieces, and yet it also gives us the time, an individual is made up of physical and mental components which also react with the environment. Lewin makes it evident that it is meaningless to explain behaviour without reference to both the person and his or her environment.

Interactive studies

Although these are the main theoretical disciplines from which the concept of socialization has emerged, socialization was not studied *per se* by any of the original theorists, but has developed gradually from them as an area to be studied in its own right. Research has moved away from comparative studies of natural populations, through laboratory research frequently involving the use of systematic experimental manipulations (Danziger 1978), towards observational studies, both in the home and in other 'natural' settings (for example, schools and playgroups), with more of an emphasis on interactional strategies (Snyder and Ickes 1985; Kernis et al 1993). Some of the earlier studies used film (for example, Trevarthen 1974) or tape recordings to collect information. Today videotapes appear to be one of the main sources of data collection and allow for a more detailed analysis than was previously possible from observation alone.

The past two decades or so have seen a proliferation in observational interactive studies of the normal child, far too many to be reviewed easily or comprehensively. In contrast there is a dearth of studies relating to the socialization of deaf children (although research into their communication and education is increasing steadily). Pioneering work in this field has been undertaken in the USA by Mindel and Vernon (1971); Furth (1978); Schlesinger and Meadow – both together (1972) and independently (Meadow 1980; Schlesinger 1978, 1985) – and Altschuler (1974); but very little elsewhere in the world. Therefore interactive studies with normal-hearing children are used, where appropriate, to illustrate areas of particular relevance to the deaf child.

Caregiver–child interactions

There seems to be general agreement among researchers that the primary caregivers have crucial significance regarding a child's development. It has been argued that adults have overwhelming power in the socialization process because the infant or small child (whether deaf or hearing) is ignorant of any alternatives, and it is adults who confront the child with the world (Berger and Berger 1978; McCandless 1969; Hart et al 1990; Schlesinger 1985). However, there is some disagreement over whether the process is unidirectional (where adults have a major effect on the infant), as suggested by Kerckoff (1972), or more of a two-way situation, with the infant acting as a trigger in the interactive process (Bell 1971).

As research in this field accumulates, more and more studies are suggesting that infants do have an important role in interactions, and may selectively reinforce parental behaviour (Bell 1974; Collins and Schaffer 1975; Bakeman and Brown 1980), although Goldberg (1988), who studied the impact of medical problems (prematurity, developmental delay and cystic fibrosis) on infant–mother attachment, found some support for the notion that the mother plays a more powerful role than the infant in shaping the quality of the attachment relationship. She concluded that it is normally very difficult to disrupt good mothering, even with the stressful demands of an ill or handicapped child.

Studies of maternal deprivation and social isolation have clearly indicated that, without social stimulation, children suffer emotionally and even physically (for example, Spitz 1945, 1946, 1965; Robertson 1958; Lewis and Freedle 1973; Lane 1977). Lewis and Freedle have shown that sensory dysfunction can lead to impairment in the social realm, thus a deaf child is at an immediate disadvantage compared with hearing children.

Schaffer and Emerson (1973) have argued that, although attachment to the mother is very important, to focus enquiry on the child's relationship with the mother alone would give a misleading impression, because other people are also important in the child's life. Since that time an increasing number of researchers have focused on peer group interaction. Some research has also been undertaken which suggests that the neighbourhood where a child lives may influence both child and adolescent behaviour after the preschool age (Brooks-Gunn et al 1993).

Peer group studies

According to Corsaro (1981), the discovery of friendship is a major step in the child's acquisition of social knowledge. Through interaction with peers children learn that they can negotiate social bonds on the basis of their personal needs and the demands of their social context. They also learn that peers will not always accept them immediately; often a child must convince others of his or her merits as a playmate, and sometimes he or she must anticipate and accept exclusion (p.207).

In a study of peer social skills in toddlers by same-age and mixed-age children, Brownell (1990) found that toddlers were able to adjust their behaviour to the social characteristics of different partners, and that the sociability and responsiveness of a partner may be salient influences on interaction. This finding has implications for deaf children, who begin their interaction with hearing peers with disadvantages with communication (see

Chapter 3).

Mead (1934) argued that children take on the roles and attitudes of significant others around them. The way we see ourselves is partly in response to how others see us, so that if attitudes towards the child are unaccepting, or if the child perceives that others see him as different, he may come to see himself as unacceptable or different in some way and act on the basis of that difference (see also Chapter 6). Evidence for this has been given by Tiffen (1986), who found that children rejected by their peers showed minimum improvement over time, even when given training in social skills.

A study involving the integration of hearing and deaf preschoolers (Vandell et al 1982) found that hearing preschoolers frequently and persistently refused to interact with profoundly deaf peers. The study involved an attempt to modify this behaviour. After intervention, which involved a three-week training programme that included discussions about the meaning of deafness, the opportunity to practise communication techniques with deaf children and free play interactions with deaf children, significant differences were found. Instead of an expected increase in interaction, hearing children exposed to the above intervention began interacting significantly less with their deaf peers than did the control group. They also became less responsive to the deaf children's attempts to interact with them than did the control group.

An earlier study (George and Vandell 1981) found that hearing children fail to modify the way they initiate interaction with a deaf peer to take into account the lack of hearing. They found deaf children to be persistent initiators of interaction, while at the same time encountering interaction difficulties because they were more likely to be refused. Also, the hearing children were more likely to initiate their interactions inappropriately by gesturing or speaking to the back of the deaf children. This study suggested that, rather than a lack of communication skills, the greatest difficulty for deaf children may be that of interacting with others who do not know their language.

A further study by Lederberg et all (1986), looking at ethnic, gender and age preferences among deaf and hearing preschool peers, found that the only effect of deafness was to decrease the amount of gender segregation that occurred. Their results suggest that the development of playmate preference is not dependent on intergroup language differences or spoken cultural messages. They also found that preschoolers of different social groups have different social experiences.

The development of social skills has been found to be a crucial determinant of children's peer relationships, and unpopular children frequently lack social skills, although coaching in these skills can improve peer relations (Asher and Renshaw 1981). Dodge et all (1986) aimed to develop a model of social exchange in children. They found that how a child behaved when first meeting peers significantly predicted the peers' judgement of him or her, and those judgements in turn significantly predicted the peers' behaviour towards the child.

A series of studies has been undertaken on the concept of 'learned helplessness' (for example, Dweck 1975; Dweck and Repucci 1973; Diener and Dweck 1978, 1980; Goetz and Dweck 1980; Fincham et al 1987; Fincham et al 1989). Helplessness in social situations is the perceived inability to overcome rejection. Fincham and Hokoda (1987) found that children who are rejected and neglected by peers are likely to manifest learned helplessness in social situations.

These findings have important implications in terms of self-esteem and later emotional health, and are supported by several studies which showed people with low self-esteem unable to use strategies for self-enhancement in social situations (for example, Baumeister et al 1989; Brown et al 1988; Tice 1991). Children who experience poor peer relations tend to have behavioural and psychological problems (Spence 1987; Cramer 1990; Henderson et al 1981), and popular children have been shown to be more positive about themselves on a variety of dimensions, and also to have higher self-esteem than average children (Boivin and Begin 1989). (Self-esteem is discussed in Chapter 6).

From the research undertaken it appears that caregiver–child relationships have importance in later friendship development (for example, Vandell and Wilson 1987; Hart et al 1990; Rubin 1980; Asher et all 1977). Children learn skills of friendship not only from each other, but also from parents and teachers. Vandell and Wilson found that children who participated more in turn-taking with parents also participated more in turn-taking with peers; while Hart et all found that children of mothers who were more power-assertive in their disciplinary styles tended to be less accepted by peers, and tended to expect successful outcomes for unfriendly-assertive methods for resolving peer conflict (for example, threatening to hit another child). As expected, those who used friendly-assertive strategies were more accepted by their peers.

Rubin has argued that parents and teachers who are sensitive to the needs and circumstances of the child play a crucial role in facilitating the development of friendship skills, and that, rather than pushing social skills indiscriminately, adults should respect the differences between children that motivate some to establish friendly relations with many others, some to concentrate on one or two close relationships, and some to spend a good deal of time by themselves.

Moving towards a multidisciplinary perspective

As shown by the profusion and divergence of debates that surround it, socialization remains a highly complex concept. It occurs through the intricate forces and links within and between individuals, pairs, triads, groups, societies, institutions, and even international and global relationships. Throughout the literature it is generally agreed that much ignorance still remains about the actual process of socialization (in 1974 Richards commented that, because of its complexity, the most impressive thing about the infant's social development was our ignorance of the processes involved), and many researchers have argued the need for the development of assessment tools and research strategies to detect the changing effects of emergent behaviours (for example, Bell 1974; Damon 1977; Grimshaw 1977; Lewis and Rosenblum 1979b; Huston 1983; Dowdney et al 1985; Schaffer and Collis 1986).

The socialization of every child is intricately bound up with three areas:

- the individual characteristics of the child (genetic make-up, personality, physical characteristics, etc.);
- features of the society into which the child is born (the family, educational system, political system, religious system, etc.);
- the interactions in which the child participates.

The ways in which significant other people react in that child's life are in turn affected by their own characteristics, systems and interactions. All of these are constantly changing over time. I argue that it is a perspective which begins before conception and continues after death, in the sense that individuals involved in the socialization of a child have themselves previously been through the process and carry with them their own patterns of behaviour from their own experience, which in turn was born out of the experience of those who socialized them.

According to Hargreaves (1985), over the past twenty years there has been a radical shift away from the behavioural approach to understanding socialization, and now three broad characteristics are emphasized. These are:

- stress on the reciprocal nature of the relationship between the child and its environment, and the symbiotic system formed by the two;
- a shift towards the cognitive approach, with emphasis on the active part played by the child in imposing meaning on the world;
- a new emphasis on the ecological approach, which argues that no single relationship (for example, mother and child) can be studied adequately without taking into account significant others in what is a highly complex network of relationships.

Schaffer (1986) suggests that failure to take an interactionist view is probably the single most important reason why we do not have an adequate socialization theory, and claims that we remain ignorant as to how socialization influences produce socialized children. People have ideas and develop beliefs that are based on what they experience, and these ideas and beliefs may not necessarily connect with those of others. People have different levels of intelligence, awareness, openness, empathy, compassion, aggression, etc., and mistakes can occur through a lack of understanding. We create our own reality from the input we receive and from what we transmit. Each person perceives the world through their own frame of reference, so each views the world differently.

Socialization is a continuous, ever-changing, dynamic process. Changes can occur within the individual because of internal events, or because of external events, and individuals can influence change in others through their own behaviour according to their own perception of reality.

Partly linked to the work of Lewin (1952), with his concept of field theory, I have attempted to draw together the factors which affect the process of socialization. Field theory takes into consideration the situation as a whole, rather than isolated incidents, and Lewin insisted that it is meaningless to explain behaviour without reference to both the person and his or her environment. In the same way, socialization cannot be construed in isolation but needs to be studied as a whole – the individual characteristics of a person; the systems or institutions into which they are born and live, and the interactions within those systems and institutions.

Individual characteristics

Within each individual are the characteristics which go to make up that unique person. I hypothesize that these include physical, social, emotional, intellectual, biochemical, intuitive and spiritual aspects (see Figure 2.1), all of which are linked to one another, and there is an interplay of interaction between them, with changes in one affecting changes in other areas – for example, hormone changes, which are biochemical, can affect mood, which is emotional (for example, in the case of changes in thyroid function). A traumatic event could possibly affect all of them.

Each person develops their own concept of reality, according to their own experience, knowledge, understanding, and view of the world.

Interactions

Cottrell (1969) has argued that the self is not a 'thing' but a process (p.549), and these internal dimensions are constantly in operation in greater or lesser degrees within each individual, and will in turn affect interaction with

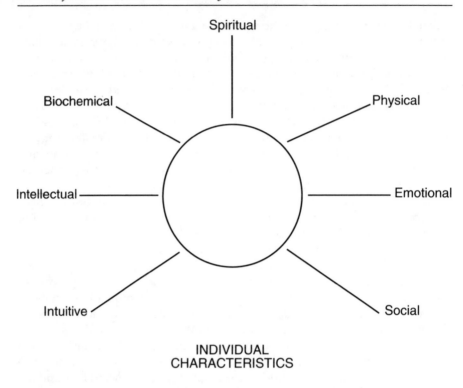

INDIVIDUAL
CHARACTERISTICS

Figure 2.1   Internal dimensions which make up an individual

others. For example, the individual's emotions towards themselves and the other person – love, anger, fear, joy, etc.; how they view the other person in relation to themselves – superior, inferior, equal (this is dependent on their ideas and beliefs, knowledge and previous experience); what they think the motives for the interaction are, etc., will all have a bearing on the process of the interaction.

Results of these interchanges become manifest in the forms of behaviour displayed by the individuals. For instance, the emotion of anger may be triggered through an interaction, but how a person expresses that anger in his or her behaviour depends on a number of different factors, including patterns set up in childhood. Interaction between people becomes increasingly complex as more people are involved.

Social factors: institutions, norms, etc.

The features of the society in which an individual lives will also have a major effect on the way that person is socialized. The family is likely to be the most influential factor initially, but the education system, legal institution, economic system, religion, and other organizations (for example, Scouts or Guides) also play an important role in the socialization process (see Figure 2.2).

Because the process of socialization can be located in a time continuum from before conception to beyond death, different systems or institutions will have greater or lesser influences as life progresses. These influences can be continuous (for example, the economy or religion into which a person is born may have a profound effect on them throughout their life); intermittent (for example, education or religion could be abandoned or discarded, and then picked up again later in life), or may have only a very small effect. Some are post-childhood influences (for example, employment, marriage or parenthood). Other rare external factors may also affect socialization (for example, being struck by lightning!).

The socializing influences

In order to attempt to simplify the notion of socialization, Figure 2.3 represents a conceptual framework model of the socializing influences which affect an individual.

The individual has been enlarged in the diagram, and will include all

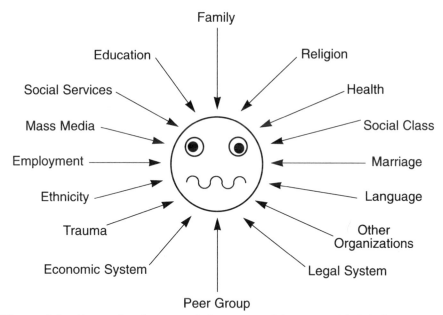

Figure 2.2   Example of some of the external factors which influence socialization

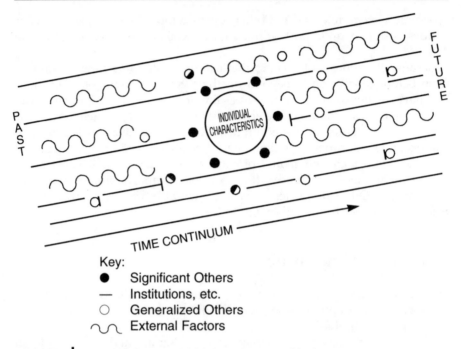

Key:
- ● Significant Others
- — Institutions, etc.
- ○ Generalized Others
- ∿ External Factors

(*Note:* The **I** denotes influences which have happened in the past, e.g. nursery school, or have yet to occur, e.g. marriage)

Figure 2.3 Diagrammatic representation of the socializing influences on one individual

those internal dimensions previously considered that go to make up a person. The dark circles closest to the individual indicate significant other people in that person's life (parents, siblings, friends, teachers, etc.) while the clear circles represent, in G.H. Mead's (1934) terms, the 'generalized others' – those people who play a part in the person's life to a lesser extent (some are represented as half-dark and half-light circles, indicating a more involved role, and all have their own internal characteristics which affect their own interactions). Systems or institutions are represented as straight lines, while other external factors are shown as wavy lines. Because life occurs in a time continuum, a vertical line is used to denote influences which have happened in the past (for example, nursery school, or people who have moved away or died) and events which are yet to happen (such as marriage, or people who are yet to be met or born).

So, as a child develops, all the factors which influence socialization are in a constant state of change. In Piaget's terms (1951, 1953), the child is 'assimilating' knowledge and 'accommodating' it, exploring and making sense of the world, developing a sense of reality, learning how to fit in with others, and learning what is acceptable behaviour within that particular society. Over time the child will become an adult, and will become an influencing factor, in turn, on the next generation, and thus the socialization process is perpetuated. In order to gain a deeper understanding of the concept of socialization, incidents must be located in both experience and time. Sequence does not necessarily mean that one event influences another. Some occurrences may not have important consequences, whereas others may be vitally important. It is difficult to identify those incidents which are important because so many factors are occurring simultaneously.

Lewin strongly emphasized that 'the full empirical reality of human experience and behaviour must be comprehended in a scientific manner' (Cartwright 1959); and field theory holds that events are determined by forces acting on them in an immediate field, rather than by forces acting at a distance (Lippitt 1968). In rejecting the notion of 'action at a distance', Lewin (1952) argued strongly that any behaviour or other psychological change depends only on the psychological field at that time. He claimed that historical problems or previous experience are important only in the sense of causal chains which create the present situation, and the psychological past and future are simultaneous parts of the psychological field existing at a given time.

Brunswick (1943) has argued that this view was limited, and that by leaving out certain physical and sociological factors Lewin excluded the most dynamic aspects of psychology.

I argue that Lewin's theory can be considered in terms of a 'snapshot' which incorporates everything that is happening at that moment in time. Since his theory was produced, dynamic aspects of interaction have begun to be incorporated into the understanding of socialization (Hargreaves 1985). Individual factors such as language development have moved from experimental observation, through tape recordings of mother–child conversations into the new era of the video recorder, with other significant people also being included. Far more information is obtained in this manner than was previously possible.

Instead of a still photograph, I suggest that socialization needs to be considered more as a moving picture, such as might be obtained from a multidimensional video camera (which has yet to be invented). We do not yet have either the terminology or the equipment to describe the process of socialization adequately. Categorizations must be provisional, and some are subjective, but, as technology advances, more tools will be developed. Computers may be the key to a deeper awareness of the process, or perhaps some new equipment not yet designed. Not so many years ago computers, holograms and space travel were in the realms of science fantasy. Now they are an accepted part of life for many people. It may eventually be possible to take all factors into account in such a way that the process will be fully understood, but at this stage only small inroads can be made.

The concept of socialization has been studied by theorists from many disciplines.[3] From an analysis of the literature on socialization I conclude that it is not possible to tackle this concept from any one school of thought alone, but that it must be considered as multifaceted. It appears from the literature that there is a gradual movement towards a multidisciplinary perspective (the main disciplines in this field being psychology, sociology, anthropology and biology), which is necessary for a detailed understanding of the process of socialization. Attempting to draw all the factors together is one small step in the direction of an eventual all-encompassing theory of socialization.

Beliefs, attitudes and implications

It is well documented from early studies that the attitude of parents can be seen to have considerable effect on the performance of children, and that parental encouragement is an extremely important factor in socialization (this has been demonstrated, for example, by McClelland and Friedman 1952; Rosen 1956; Sears et al 1957; Douglas 1964; Rosen and D'Andrade 1973; and Hess and Shipman 1965, among others).[4] More recent studies have shown that relationships with parents are crucial for primary caring, nurturing and teaching roles (Dowdney et al 1985; Schaffer and Collis 1986), as well as being a factor in the psychological health of the child (for example, Masterton and Rinsley 1975; Henderson et al 1981; Huston 1983; Cramer 1990; Bezirganian et al 1993).

Drawing from the work of George Kelly (1955, 1963) a basic premise has been developed by McGillicuddy-De Lisi et al (1979), that parents actively construct belief systems about children on the basis of their own experiences.[5] The beliefs are used to categorize events, and guide parental behaviour towards their child. What the parent believes the child to be capable of is likely to be a major influence on parental practices.

Parental belief systems can be modified as a result of new or discrepant experiences, and each person in the family may have an effect on the belief system, so parental behaviour may alter in order to be consistent with changes in belief.

As parental practices change, so do their impact on the child, and additional feedback from each child in the family must be dealt with in the context of the belief system continuously being constructed by the parent. Thus, within the limited environment of the home, parent affects child and child affects parent (McGillicuddy-De Lisi et al 1979, p.94). This is supported by Rubin and Mills (1988).

If a normal child is influenced by parental belief systems, then questions arise about what happens to those belief systems when a child is diagnosed as deaf. Does the age of onset and cause of hearing loss make a difference to the belief system? If, as McGillicuddy-De Lisi et al suggest, parents have their own beliefs (from which they construct their belief systems) about what their children are capable of achieving based on their own experiences, because severe or profound deafness is relatively uncommon in this country, it possibly falls outside the experience of many parents until their child is diagnosed. To date I am unaware of any research in this area.

Togonu-Bickersteth and Odebiyi (1985) have studied the influence of the Nigerian Yoruba people's beliefs about abnormality on the socialization of deaf children, and found that traditional beliefs affected the relationship between mother and child. Beliefs relating to sin and handicap, a concern for perfection of body and mind, as well as the traditional reliance by parents on adult children for support in old age, all complicated the relationship and led to poor affectional bonds between mothers and their deaf children.

There is some controversy in the research about the age at which the concept of belief develops. Gopnik (1990) argued that before the age of 5 years there is a lack of concept of belief, although Wellman and Estes (1986) found that even 3-year-old children have remarkably sophisticated understanding of the differences between physical objects and mental entities – thoughts, dreams and images; and Gopnik and Graf (1988) found evidence to suggest that children learn about the causal relation between the world and the mind between 3 and 5 years old.

However, Bartsch and Wellman (1989) found that even 3-year-old children attributed actions to true or false beliefs, demonstrating an understanding of belief not evident in previous research.

Work has been carried out by Alessandri and Wozniak (1987) on the child's awareness of parental beliefs concerning the child. They investigated adolescents' and pre-adolescents' awareness of the beliefs that parents hold, by examining patterns of agreement between parents, and between parents and children, concerning the child's likely behaviour in a variety of ways. They found that families varied widely in intrafamilial situations, and that adolescents were more accurate in predicting parental beliefs than pre-adolescents. They claim that it stands to reason that the beliefs children extract from their experience are likely to reflect both their developing cognitive skills and their changing social environment. In a follow-up study, Alessandri and Wozniak (1989) found that the accuracy of children's predictions of parental beliefs increased sharply between ages 10 to 11, and 12 to 13, but not between 15 to 16 or 17 to 18; that congruency of both mothers' and fathers' beliefs with the child's self-beliefs increased; and that, between families, overall levels of intrafamilial agreement in belief concerning the children remained remarkably stable. Their findings support the notion that changes in adolescents' understanding of their own development and of their changing relationships to parents occur within a framework of overall consistency in the level of intrafamilial agreement in belief.

Another study on the changing perceptions in children was carried out by Younger and Bokyo (1987), who examined the ability of children of different ages to encode and retrieve from memory descriptions of aggressive and withdrawn behaviours displayed by hypothetical peers. They found that, at different ages, children differ in their ability to report on aggressive and withdrawn behaviour in their peers, and found evidence of the emerging importance of social withdrawal as a social-cognitive schema underlying children's social perceptions.

These findings would seem to confirm Rogers's (1978) claim that the young child's way of perceiving others will put him at a disadvantage relative to an older child or adult. Young children will be less able to predict the behaviour of others across a range of situations and will consequently be less able to control their own behaviour with respect to the reactions and behaviour of others. He argued that as adults we perceive people in order to be able to predict the behaviour of others, control our own behaviour and influence others' behaviour, and until further research is done we can only assume that this also applies to young children.

From a review of research on parents' ideas, actions and feelings, drawing from developmental and social psychology, it appears that, as yet, little is known about how parents think and feel about social development (Goodnow 1988); and that virtually none of the knowledge that has been acquired concerns parents' perspectives on problematic as opposed to normal social development (Mills and Rubin 1990), although work is being undertaken in this area. For example, Rubin and Mills (1988) found that aggressive behaviour from children towards their peers produced stronger negative emotions in parents (that is, anger, disappointment or embarrassment) than did withdrawal, which parents found more puzzling.

When interpersonal behaviour goes wrong there is inefficiency, unhappiness and conflict between individuals and groups (Argyle 1976). If acceptance is positively related to self-esteem (Henderson et al 1981), and social support determines psychological health (Cramer 1990), then deaf children are more at risk of rejection by peers and significant others around them because of their difficulties with communication; and are therefore at greater risk of suffering emotionally.

Research is consistent in that deaf children tend to have rather more emotional problems than those who hear well (Lansdown 1980; Meadow 1980; Gregory 1976; Schlesinger and Meadow 1972; Rainer et al 1969) and are therefore more at risk of poor social relationships. Normally children learn through communication, observation, imitation and through listening.

Because they cannot hear, deaf children cannot absorb the basic everyday happenings that hearing children do.

Lansdown (1980) suggests that, as well as suffering frustration at not being able to make themselves understood, deaf children also lack the same kind of communication from adults that the hearing child receives. Rather than a long explanation, the temptation for the parent is just to say 'no' (see also Schlesinger 1978); and parents frequently resort to physical punishment and restraint rather than verbal discipline and explanation (Chess 1975; Mindel and Vernon 1971; Schlesinger and Meadow 1972).

Older deaf children and adolescents tend to be immature and withdrawn, although the rates of overt neurosis and delinquency are no higher than normal (Lansdown 1980; Denmark 1976); and the incidence of schizophrenia is equivalent in deaf and hearing people (Rainer and Altschuler 1966; Rainer et al 1969).

However, it has been suggested by Argyle (1976) that paranoia is most likely to be displayed by children who are isolated from the healthy ridicule of the peer group. He argued that paranoia is precipitated by social stresses such as failure, competition, or loss of a supporting social relationship, and that schizophrenia may be due to inadequate socialization. If deaf children are isolated because of a lack of communication skills, they may also be at greater risk of some form of mental illness in later life. (This is discussed further in Chapter 3, pages 51–2.) From studying sensory deprivation (in the blind), Klein (1962) suggested that it is interpersonal isolation, not the sensory deficit, that disrupts the child's ego or personality development, and Schlesinger (1985) has pointed out that, although the deaf population does not have a higher incidence of mental illness than normal, researchers indicate that the deaf suffer 'more problems in living' (p.106).

'Successful' socialization, leading to individual self-development and fulfilment; mutually satisfying interactions, and effective participation and involvement in such things as the education system and hearing society in general, all revolve around the major pivot of communication and language. This is discussed in the next chapter.

Notes

1   The following example may serve to clarify the differences between the three systems; for someone who is feeling hungry at a funeral:

Id –	'You've got to feed me now. I'm hungry.'
Superego –	'How can you possibly think of food at a time like this? You should know better.'
Ego –	'When we leave here we'll have something to eat.'

2   Freud's theories, which were developed over fifty years, fill 24 volumes. The beginning reader is referred to Freud (1940) (published a year after his death), and Freud (1965).

3   The reader is referred to: Zigler and Child (1973) for an overview of socialization and personality development; Goslin (1969) for socialization theory and research; Brehm et al (1981) for a comprehensive presentation of theory and research based on efforts to integrate social psychology and developmental psychology, and Smith and Cowie (1988) for an introductory psychology text on child development.

4   An attitude is a like or dislike, a positive or negative evaluation about some aspect of the world, whereas a belief is a statement about the world that a person thinks to be true (Hilgard et al 1990). According to Zimbard and Ebbesen (1970), attitudes are learned and are therefore susceptible to change, whereas beliefs are much more resistant to change.

5   A belief system may be defined as having, in some organized psychological but not necessarily logical form, every single belief about physical and social reality represented within it (Rokeach 1972).

3 Language and meaning

Introduction

Language and psychosocial development have an interactive effect (Bentler et al 1984). People vary in their influence on others and in the way they are influenced by others. Language is a major means of control. Children learn to have their needs met through language, and to gain control over their environment and other people. Language is a very powerful tool for getting what we want. It has been suggested by Farb (1977) that language cannot be separated from the totality of human behaviour. It forms the core of all our cultural concerns, arts, sciences, customs and institutions, and penetrates the experience of human beings to such an extent that neither language nor behaviour can be understood without knowledge of both. Therefore an understanding of the nature of language is vital to an understanding of the needs, development and socialization of the deaf child.

There is a wide range of variation in the development of children, which is considered to be within normal limits, in all areas, including language acquisition, and this needs to be borne in mind when studying the development of any child. However, there are well-documented vast differences in both speech and language development between deaf and hearing children, which are discussed in this chapter.

The first part of this chapter will consider the definition and concept of language and communication, followed by a theoretical overview, and the modes of communication available to the hearing-impaired in the UK. Language acquisition is then divided into three areas: normal acquisition for the hearing child; acquisition for the deaf child in the hearing home, and acquisition for the deaf child in the deaf home. This is followed by a review of some of the literature relating to studies in language acquisition.

Defining language

Although virtually everyone uses language in some form for a large proportion of the time they spend in social interaction, because of its complexity, it remains extremely difficult to define (for example, *A Dictionary of Psychology* (Drever 1974) defines it as 'a conventional system of expressive signs functioning psychologically, in the individual, as an instrument of conceptual analysis and synthesis, and, socially, as a means of intercommunication' (p.154) – which is not particularly helpful).

In its full global sense, language includes both verbal and non-verbal expression, and can be communicated aurally, visually and through touch, as well as through writing and drawing (for example, a gentle hand on the shoulder in a moment of shared sorrow can express far more than words; in the same way, a pointed finger and facial expression can give a very clear message to a child about to embark on a prohibited act, before any words have been uttered).

Each of the components which make up language have their own subdivisions. For example, speech can be divided into articulation, voice quality and expression of ideas (Robbins 1963), while non-verbal communication can include facial expression, gesture, body posture, lip pattern, fingerspelling and signs. All these components require a shared understanding of the meaning behind the actions for communication to occur. If for any reason channels are blocked, misunderstandings are likely to arise. This can have obvious and far-reaching consequences for the hearing-impaired, where a degree of blockage to the aural channel is already in effect.

It has been suggested by Terwilliger (1968) that it is precisely because people 'know' what language is from their own use of it that it is so difficult to define. He argued that many definitions, such as 'language is a communication by symbols', only repeat the fact that language is a language; they do not tell us how to recognize a language. He considered that there are four characteristics that language must have, and defined it as: a system of behaviours and potential behaviours that may influence the behaviour of other people; that are relevant or appropriate to states of affairs in the user's environment; but are, in fact, independent of those states of affairs; and that may be inappropriate or wrong.

Another view, put forward by Greene (1986), is that conventionally language is defined as having two main functions – external communications with other people, and internal representations of a person's own thoughts – and that whole books have been written trying to answer the questions 'what is language?' and 'what is communication?'. Greene argues that language seems to depend both on universal knowledge shared by all human beings, and on highly specific knowledge restricted to that particular society. For Greene, language simultaneously reflects and shapes our attitudes and actions within the society in which we live and, despite all the general knowledge that speakers may have in common, communication is very limited without a shared language.

Language is a symbolic means of understanding ourselves in relation to others, and the inability to communicate effectively affects all areas of subsequent development (Mead 1934). According to Farb (1977), until language has made sense of experience, that experience is meaningless; and without an adequate means of communication there is social isolation, frustration and depression.

A theoretical overview of language

From the theoretical work undertaken to develop an understanding of the concept of language, two main viewpoints seem to have emerged. Language is seen by some as an institution and by others as a social process.

The structural functionalist view of language as an institution stems from the work of Durkheim, who developed his ideas during the late nineteenth century. Durkheim saw language as playing an important part in social cohesion and norm maintenance in society. He argued that a social institution maintains the norms in society and creates a solidarity which holds society together. From this viewpoint, language is an institution because it is external to the self and has a coercive effect. People have to use the language of their society in order to be able to communicate with others. Anyone who cannot communicate is penalized by society in general. Language is fixed and only changes very slowly over time.

On the other hand, the social phenomenological view of language as a social process can be linked to the work of Mead (1934) and, more recently, to such authors as Berger and Berger (1978), and Berger and Luckman (1967). From this viewpoint, language is seen as part of a continuing process of social development in which the individual comes to make sense of the world through language and interaction with others.

Each of these viewpoints has implications for both deaf individuals and the deaf population in general, in terms of meanings and interactions. Some of these implications will be addressed in the following chapters.

As with child development, several theories have been put forward as to how language is actually acquired. Early thought in the behaviourist school came from Watson (1913), who considered that speech processes were really motor habits in the larynx, and thinking was entirely made up of learned speech.

Skinner (1957) agreed with Watson and decided that all language develops by means of a conditioning stimulus–response mechanism whereby the child learns speech by positive and negative reinforcement. For Skinner, learning was essentially passive, and language a collection of words, phrases and sentences – a set of habits which were acquired accidentally depending on experience. Human learning processes were essentially the same as the learning processes demonstrated in laboratory experiments on animals. He insisted that language must be studied in terms of what can be observed, and rejected the word 'language' in favour of the term 'verbal behaviour'. Traditional explanations of language in terms of 'meanings', 'ideas' and 'mind' were unscientific because they could not be observed, measured, or experimentally manipulated (Open University 1975).

In 1959 Chomsky attacked this viewpoint, claiming that behaviourists were using scientific terminology and statistics to cover up their inability to account for the fact that human language is radically different from animal communication. Chomsky believed that the structure of language is determined by the structure of the human mind, and that certain properties characteristic of language are universal to the whole of the human species regardless of race or class, or of differences in intellect, personality or physical attributes (Lyons 1977).

Chomsky (1968) argued that the fundamental characteristic of language is its creativity. A human being can speak and understand sentences they have never heard before. To explain this he has put forward the idea of a 'language acquisition device'. This suggests that infants have a universal, innate ability to understand how to use human language, regardless of which language they eventually come to speak. Chomsky claims that there are two aspects to sentence structure: surface structure (the utterances made) and deep structure, which requires understanding and interpretation to give meaning to words. He argued that Skinner could only handle the structural complexities of sentences by rejecting the concept of deep structures.

Although influenced by Watson, Mead (1934) also went beyond the behaviourist approach, arguing that people are not simply the outcome of their social environment, but that human beings give meaning to their world, and attach meaning to language. As a person develops he becomes aware of himself as himself ('I'), and himself in relation to others ('me', that is, the me that I can see), through taking on different roles in the socialization process. He also develops a sense of 'other', both significant other (key figures in his life such as parents, siblings, etc.) and the generalized other (society as a whole), and learns to act in accordance with these images. This is a continuing process throughout life, and language is a part of this social process.

Mead argued that Watson, by seeing language as a learned serial order of behaviour, missed the essential point that we attach meaning to language. Mead identifies two levels of social interaction (Blumer 1969): one that occurs when there is no interpretation, and another where, by the use of significant symbols, a person interprets the meaning of the situation in relation to the context in which they are participating (symbolic interaction). So Mead sees the self as a process rather than a structure, and language is a dynamic part of that process.

In contrast to Chomsky's view that individuals have the general capacity to create new structures that they have never been exposed to, and the behaviourist view that speech is all given to an individual, another viewpoint emerged which suggests that culture and language are inextricably bound. Names associated with this view include Wittgenstein, Whorf and Sapir.

Whorf (1956) argued that it is culture that determines language, and suggested that the individual speaks or thinks in a particular way because he is constrained by the linguistic system in his mind. For Whorf, different languages influence thinking in different ways – what a person thinks, and the way he sees things, is determined by the language in which he thinks. Sapir (1966) argued that people are 'at the mercy of the particular language that they speak', and that the real world is built up on the language habits of the group. He suggested that no two languages represent the same reality, but that two different societies will inhabit two distinctly different worlds because the meanings put into them through language are not the same in the two societies.

This view was also put forward by Wittgenstein (1953), who argued that 'the limits of my language mean the limits of my world'. He claimed that the meaning of a word is to be understood through its use, and that, until experience is understood, through language, that experience has no meaning; yet language can limit the capacity to express certain ideas or opinions.

Work undertaken on the relationship between thought and language (on both deaf and hearing people) suggests that thought and language are separate processes (Furth 1961, 1966, 1973; Oleron 1953; Whorf 1950; Cromer 1979), although, obviously, interaction exists between them.

Furth (1961, 1966) studied cognition, intelligence and language development in deaf children and found that, although language experience may increase the efficiency of concept formation in a certain situation, it was not a necessary prerequisite for the development of the basic capacity to abstract and generalize. He demonstrated that logical, intelligent thinking is independent of language, and argued that intelligence is not dependent on language, but that comprehension and use of ready-made language is dependent on intelligence (Furth 1966).

Vygotsky (1966) proposed that thought and language have separate roots prelingually, which become linked as verbal speech, suggesting that the relation of thought to word is a continual back and forth process so that thought is not merely expressed in words, but comes into existence through them. He postulated that, if children are confronted with a problem which is slightly too complicated for them, they use speech to break the problem into several parts, so that each part becomes an independent problem.

Words mean nothing by themselves. It is only when a thinker makes use of them that they stand for anything (Ogden and Richards 1923); and the only connection that exists between a word and the thing it stands for is whichever association the speech community has decided to make (Farb 1977).

Yet language is the most basic meaning system familiar to everyone, and helps to shape, discuss, perceive and generally structure the universe (Hughes 1978). Heal (1989) pointed out that we ascribe meaning or content to utterance, psychological states, etc.; sometimes we receive contradictory statements, and we have a variety of labels and techniques for assimilating and dealing with them. (She suggested, for example, that we might diagnose a slip of the tongue, or look for deep psychological ambivalences in order to explain them.)

It is possible to have a situation where two contradictory messages are given simultaneously, in such a way that it is impossible for the receiver to interpret the meaning behind the interaction. Bateson et al (1976) termed this the 'double-bind' situation, and argued that, if this situation is continuous over a prolonged period of time, mental illness on the part of the receiver can result. Laing (1965, 1976) also argued that mental illness can result from confusion or 'mystification' in interpersonal relationships, because of differences in the interpretation of meanings in a social situation.[1] He argued that families set up defences in order to avoid real conflicts, and that delusions and hallucinations can be shown to be rational in the context of these family relationships. Both Bateson et al and Laing were concerned with developing a theory of schizophrenia, which they saw as a social construct rather than a physical illness.[2]

Apart from the multifarious internal factors which affect meaning and understanding, different levels and forms of communication operate in face-to-face interaction (see Figure 3.1). For example, as in Figure 3.1(a), people may communicate effectively in a variety of ways, that is, they may be conversing using speech or sign language, or communicating in other ways, such as with eye contact, touch, etc. A mother playing with a prelingual baby who is babbling and handing her a toy is communicating with her child, even though the actual use of words may only be one-sided. People generally know when they are communicating well, and there is a sense of mutual satisfaction. This situation can also apply with negative messages and feedback, providing that A and B share a mutual understanding of what is being conveyed. For example, two small children having an argument:

A: 'I hate you'
B: 'I hate you too and I'm never going to play with you again',

are clearly communicating with each other, even though the content of the communication is negative.

Sometimes, as in Figure 3.1(b), one person is communicating (or thinks they are) and the other is not. There can be a variety of reasons for this. For example, the non-communicating person may be refusing to communicate (because they are sulking, angry, afraid, rebellious, etc.), or may be unable to communicate. This could be because of a physical or mental impairment on the part of B (for example, speech dysfunction or brain dysfunction, etc.), or a result of an inability to comprehend what is being communicated (for example, foreign language, poor speech articulation; confused or muddled speech such as may be found in people with schizophrenia, or in very young children developing language, etc.). In this situation A is satisfied with the communication but B is not. Another common occurrence in interaction, illustrated in Figure 3.1(c), is where neither party is communicating but both are aware of it. Again this can be due to a refusal to communicate (for example, 'I'm never speaking to you again'), or to an inability to make sense out of the interaction or gain a feeling of satisfaction from the communication.

Figure 3.1(d) illustrates a fourth possibility, in which neither party is communicating, but neither is aware of it. In this case both A and B put their own meaning and interpretation into the situation and derive satisfaction from the encounter.

These examples imply that an understanding or interpretation of meaning or intention is necessary for mutually satisfying communication to occur. Without shared meaning, in most encounters there will be confusion or frustration, and this may in turn lead to withdrawal from, or avoidance of contact with, the other party.

Modes of communication

As has been discussed above, language is not simply a means of communicating information, it is also a very important means of establishing relationships with other people (Trudgill 1981). In its broadest sense, language includes facial expression, touch, gesture, lip reading, speech, writing, drawing, conventional signs, fingerspelling and pantomime (Wolff 1976), and Argyle (1976) points out that, when speech is impossible, gesture language develops. This happens in noisy factories, on racecourses

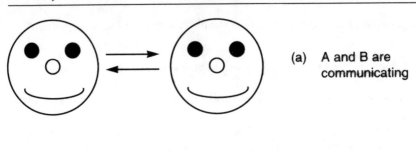

(a)   A and B are
      communicating

(b)   A is communicating,
      B is not

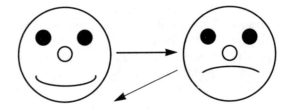

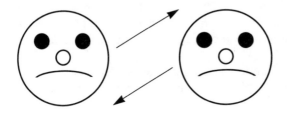

(c)   Neither A nor B is
      communicating, and
      both are aware of it

(d)   Neither A nor B is
      communicating, but
      neither is aware of it

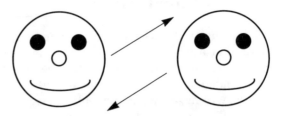

Figure 3.1   Communication

and in underwater swimming, etc.

According to West (1985) the loss of hearing, or the congenital absence of hearing, is a social and communications disaster for which the deaf person must compensate as well as possible early in life, or as soon as hearing is lost, by alternative means of communication, otherwise the individual will suffer devastating social isolation, and all aspects of a child's life will be affected – cognitive as well as social. Deaf children born of hearing parents have grave problems because neither they nor their parents know how to communicate with each other.

The deaf have a choice between two modes of communication – oral and manual – and between two languages – in the UK the languages are usually spoken English and British Sign Language (BSL).

Klima and Bellugi (1979) have argued that a deaf child with deaf parents will develop normally if the parents use sign language, as this becomes an adequate substitute for speech and hearing. The child learns to comprehend signs and to progress along much the same course by which a hearing child develops language.

Arguments regarding which communication method is best for deaf children, particularly in the field of education, have been continuing for many years (Adams 1987b). These arguments and other issues surrounding the communication controversy are discussed in detail in later chapters.

This section is concerned with a brief explanation of the different modes of communication open to the hearing-impaired. These include: oralism, cued speech, fingerspelling, British Sign Language, Signed English, Signs-Supporting English, other signing systems, and Total Communication.

Oralism

Children educated with this method use only speech and lip reading to communicate. Signs of any sort are strongly discouraged or even prevented (Adams 1987b). Listening and speaking require considerable effort and concentration by the severely hearing-impaired child, and signing is much easier. Oralists argue that, if the child is allowed to sign, the ability to develop speech is inhibited. The normal-hearing child is thought to understand a significant amount of language by 1 year of age, and 80 per cent of language development will have occurred by 3 years of age. Oralism assumes that the brain of a hearing-impaired child remains capable of learning speech and language at least until puberty and perhaps beyond (Lenneberg 1967). Adams has pointed out that many others subscribe to the view that there is a critical period for most children during the first few years of life when language development is at a premium, and that, if hearing-impaired children are not taught communication skills within this period, they may never acquire them.

Lip reading is a skill which, although it can be taught to a certain extent, appears to depend on possession of certain innate abilities (Hough 1983). It requires an understanding of the words being spoken, and can be very confusing, as many letters cannot be identified from the lip pattern. Much lip reading is guesswork. McCormick (1979) pointed out that there is no doubt that deaf children are exposed to a very different form of language than hearing children, and claimed that no single speech sound can be identified with certainty from purely visual information. This view supports that of Reed (1976), who suggested that the deaf are expected to learn a linguistic code when they see only three consonants: PBM as one, FV as a second, and Th as a third (and commented that it is no wonder the majority of deaf people develop a bizarre language system); Lowell (1959), who claimed that the best lip readers in a one-to-one situation only understand about 26 per cent of what is said; and Vernon (1972, 1976), who argued that, in group situations, with people who have moustaches, protruding teeth, etc., the situation is much worse. Vernon (1981) also argued that a deaf child in a hearing class may only get 5–20 per cent of information through lip reading, which means that learning is extremely difficult, and discussion is impossible.

Cued speech

In order to ease some of the confusion involved with lip reading, cued speech was developed by Cornett (1967). This uses eight different handshapes in four different positions close to the speaker's mouth to enable the child to discriminate the lip movement. As Adams (1987b) pointed out, cued speech was developed as an aid to teach English to deaf children, and not as an exclusive signing system (the aim was to phase out the cues as the person becomes more proficient at lip reading). Again, it requires an understanding of both English and lip reading to be effective.

Fingerspelling

With fingerspelling, the 26 letters of the alphabet are spelled out on the fingers as a code for English. The British deaf community use a two-handed alphabet (as do Australian deaf people), while certain other countries, such as France and the USA, use a one-handed alphabet; there is also a method of spelling letters on the hand for use with the deaf-blind (RNID 1981).

Historically, fingerspelling has been used as a means of communication between certain communities of different dialects for a long time. For example, the manual number system was used as far back as the preliterate medieval times in the marketplace in Scotland (Tumim 1975, cited in Montgomery 1976, p.3). Adams (1987b) has argued that, on its own, it is a slow means of communication, but speed will depend on the proficiency of the users.

Fingerspelling is frequently taught to children in junior schools and in organizations such as Cubs and Brownies.

British Sign Language (BSL)

British Sign Language (BSL) is a method of communication used by the deaf which is now beginning to be regarded as the indigenous language of deaf people in the UK (Montgomery 1981b).[3] It is a language in its own right, with its own grammar and vocabulary (Montgomery 1981b; Woll and Lawson 1981; Hough 1983; Brennan et al 1984; Deuchar 1984; EEC 1988), which involves a combination of signs, fingerspelling and non-manual signals, such as facial expression and body movement. It is a completely separate language with its own structure that does not correspond to English grammar, therefore it is not a code for spoken language, but is a language that uses a visual channel rather than an auditory one.

Klima and Bellugi (1979) argued that, until research into sign language began, people thought that sign was limited to expressing concrete ideas, was a collection of gestures, and had no grammar of its own. Since the 1960s there has been an upsurge of interest in language generally. For example, Bernstein's work on social class and language variations (1971, 1973) led people to question the previously accepted norm that standard spoken English was the only correct way to speak, and that any other way was inferior. Similar explorations were undertaken in other countries – for example, Labov (1972) in the USA. Brennan (1976) claimed that the same arguments apply to BSL as Labov found with his studies on black vernacular English – that it was a 'primitive' and 'inadequate' language – yet neither claim stood up to linguistic study. She argued that, in the same way, statements in the Lewis Report (DES 1968) that sign is illogical, ungrammatical, unsystematic, primitive, inadequate and non-linguistic were based on impression, not on objective evidence.

Possibly, because BSL is not based on English, assumptions about it by hearing people have been based on a knowledge of English (Brennan 1981). Since it has been studied by linguists, BSL has been shown to have its own grammatical structure. It is conceptually different from English, and cannot be understood in terms of English, in the same way that the language of the Hopi Indians studied by Whorf (1950) was found to be conceptually different and yet was no less a language.

In June 1988 the European Parliament officially recognized the national sign languages of member states (EEC 1988; see also page 89). This was warmly welcomed by the British deaf community, particularly as BSL has only been regarded as a language in its own right since the late 1970s.

Approximately 50 000 people in the UK use BSL (*See Hear*, BBC 1 26 November 1989), which is a very small number compared with the English-speaking majority, but compares favourably with, for example, the Gaelic-speaking community in the UK of 80 000 (MacKinnon and Densham 1989). In the European Community 'there are half a million profoundly deaf people and many times that number of partially hearing and deafened people' (EEC 1988).

Signed English

True (exact) Signed English uses signs taken from BSL, with artificially developed 'sign markers' to indicate tense, word endings, etc. (Adams 1987b). It is sign in English language word order, sometimes called 'manually coded English', and is used with lip reading and fingerspelling. Speech and sign are used in conjunction with each other so that pupils and teachers speak the same words that they are signing.

Signed English developed in the USA for US deaf preschool children. It was a system designed to facilitate the English language development of the preschool child by providing a reasonable semantic approximation to the usual language environment of the hearing child (Bornstein 1974). This method was first evaluated over a four-year period, while both teachers and pupils were learning Signed English, and the results were reported by Bornstein et al (1980). Despite reservations about writing a report when rapid changes were occurring (for example, new teaching aids were being developed and competence by teachers was improving as the course developed), the study demonstrated that children exposed to Signed English 'did indeed begin to acquire some considerable skill in the use of this English-based system. The order of acquisition of Sign markers, if not the pace, appeared to be roughly comparable to that noted for hearing children' (Bornstein et al, p.478). One US form of Signed Exact English has the entire system illustrated in dictionary form with instructions for clear, expressive signing, suggestions for developing additional signs, and a description of the most important principles which underlie this communication method (Gustason 1980).

In December 1979 the headteachers of several schools for deaf children in the southern region of England convened a conference which considered the spectrum of signing being used in schools for the deaf. Following this conference an advisory committee was formed, which comprised a representative from each school, and other interested bodies. The committee met for the first time on 16 January 1980, and was the embryo of the working party on Signed English (Working Party on Signed English, undated). Part of its purpose was to develop and use a sign system based on BSL but which would match the complex patterns of spoken English and which would not be dependent on lip reading. Since 1985 the working party has been producing illustrated booklets of vocabulary, mainly for teachers working with hearing-impaired children, and more will be produced as they are developed.

Other sign systems have also been developed as aids to education and communication, both for the deaf and for children with other disabilities.

Signs-Supporting English

This method uses BSL signs in English word order without sign markers, together with speech (Adams 1987b) and fingerspelling. This system is also known as 'Siglish', 'Pidgin Sign' or 'the Simultaneous Method' (Montgomery 1981b) and, according to Montgomery, is an uneasy compromise between spoken English and signs presented in the word order of English. With this method, speech may be speeded up, and spoken lip-read patterns supplement the less comprehensive sign vocabulary.

Makaton

The Makaton vocabulary was devised for non-communicating mentally handicapped people. It is based largely on gesture and single BSL signs, and can be used with or without speech. Montgomery (1981b) points out that, because it is conveyed by signs taken from BSL, it has sometimes been assumed that it can be adapted for use with deaf children, but this assumption does not take into account the way children acquire language by exposure to the full complexities of conversation, and so is needlessly restricting for the ordinary pupil. According to Hough (1983), it is not a signing system, but a vocabulary.

The Paget-Gorman systematic sign language

This is a form of Signed English which was originally devised by Sir Richard Paget in 1934 and, after his death in 1955, was further developed by his widow, Lady Paget, and Dr Pierre Gorman. It was intended for use with mentally handicapped patients in hospital, those with language defects, and deaf people (Gorman and Craig 1970, cited in Montgomery 1981b, p.2, and Craig 1976). It does not claim to be a language in its own right but is a tool for teachers to supplement other skills. Parents also learn the system.

Total Communication

Total Communication was developed by Holcombe in 1967 in the USA (Rodda and Grove 1987), and involves using a combination of speech, gestures, formal signing, fingerspelling, lip reading, reading and writing.

Conrad (1979a, 1980) has postulated that, in very deaf children, the exclusive use of spoken language fails to provide sufficient linguistic stimulation to the child's brain, parts of which may then cease to function, although this view has been contested by others, for example Arnold (1982). Supporters of Total Communication argue that, by providing sensory input through different channels – auditory and visual – the possibility of language development is enhanced. This view considers the term 'language' in its widest sense – as a system of symbols and rules for communication (Adams 1987b). Speech is only one mode of language, and Adams cites authors who argue both that Total Communication impairs speech development (Taylor 1985), and that it facilitates it (Dee et al 1982; Nix 1983). Although Rodda and Grove (1987), in a very full review of the literature on studies undertaken, quote Nix as stating: 'The results [of some of the literature on deafness] do cast considerable doubt on the efficacy of simultaneous communication' (Rodda and Grove 1987, p.181).

Total Communication has been defined by Garretson (1976) as a philosophy incorporating appropriate aural, manual and oral modes of communication in order to ensure effective communication with and among hearing-impaired persons. Denton (1976) suggested that, as a philosophy rather than a method, Total Communication allows the individual scope to develop in the best way for that person; and Vernon (1976) pointed out that, while providing a clear, understandable means of communication for all children in programmes for the hearing-impaired, it also provides all deaf and hard of hearing children with the benefits of amplification of sound. Vernon (1981) advocated using the Holcombe Plan, in which Total Communication is used. With this system the deaf child joins a class with normal-hearing children with a tutor-interpreter who interprets into sign language and gives support. The hearing pupils are given the chance to learn fingerspelling and Signed English. The aim is for meaningful social and educational integration on the playground, after school and in class. Vernon has pointed out that the Holcombe Plan has demonstrated that, for integration to occur, the hearing person has to make an effort too.

Language acquisition

The development of language is considered by Genishi and Dyson (1984) to be one of the child's most spectacular accomplishments. It begins at birth and develops throughout the lifespan, and becomes most significant as a remarkable tool that can be manipulated to help people think, learn and interact in satisfying ways. The ability to share information about intentions, ideas and feelings plays a vital role in human interaction, as knowing a partner's feelings or intentions makes it possible to anticipate their response or probable behaviour, and so plan an appropriate response (Beeghly et al 1986).

For the normal-hearing child, talk is central to most aspects of the child's life, and plays a role in the acquisition of a sense of self and achievement of social identity. Language learning has its roots in the entire social-familial situation into which children are born, and children learn by uniquely different routes (Lieven 1980). Thus language experience, understanding and development will be different for each child.

Unless there are special circumstances, the majority of hearing children from hearing homes will develop spoken language spontaneously and with relative ease. Current research (discussed later in this chapter) is beginning to demonstrate that the same is true for a deaf child in a deaf home developing a visual language, which in the UK is usually BSL. But at the present time a severely or profoundly deaf child in a hearing home appears to be at a very great disadvantage.

The prelingually deaf child has a much greater problem than a child who acquires deafness after language has developed. Deafness which is congenital, or acquired prelingually, has profound consequences, even after early diagnosis and the aid of amplification. The majority of profoundly deaf children have limited or abnormal speech, whereas if deafness occurs after language has developed, there may be comprehension difficulty and voice articulation deterioration, but there will be little effect on linguistic skills (Rosenbloom 1987).

Unless a severely or profoundly prelingually deaf child is given some alternative means of communication, he or she is in grave danger of growing up deprived linguistically, culturally and socially, with all the adverse possibilities which have been identified earlier in this chapter.

Language acquisition for the hearing child

Although the normal-hearing individual will continue language development throughout life in terms of vocabulary increase, the basic essentials of grammatical speech seem to be acquired very rapidly in one short burst, normally between the ages of $1^1/_2$ and 4 years (Open University 1975). The actual age at which a child knows the fundamental rules of their language system depends on the criteria used.

Di Vesta (1974) suggested that, if the criterion used is the child's first functionally complete (but not necessarily grammatically correct) sentences, then the rules are learned around 3 years of age. If the criterion is the child's use of language that is more grammatically correct than incorrect, then they are learned at around 5 years.

There are three major parts of language development: phonology (sounds and structures), grammar, and semantics (meaning).

Phonology

According to Crystal (1976), the sounds and structures of spoken English develop along similar lines for all children in the sense that the order in which they are mastered is common to all.[4] Although there is not yet a satisfactory explanation of the order of acquisition, from the studies which have been undertaken it is evident that a number of stages are involved.

Prior to 6 months the infant uses non-linguistic vocalizations, which range from early cries of hunger, pain and pleasure, through cooing from around 3 months, to babbling at around 6 months. According to Crystal, this is not a linguistic stage.

Between 6 and 9 months, vocalizations begin to take on some characteristics of a specific language, and pitch (intonation), rhythm and tone of voice come to be used. According to some studies, these can begin earlier (for example, Trevarthen 1974), but are not produced in a systematic way until the second half of the first year.

By 12 months most children can hold conversations with their parents in which the words are unintelligible but the intonation is clear. At this stage it is possible to detect the onset of the 'deaf voice' of a child with a profound hearing loss. Also by 12 months, most children have come to produce their first word with meaning, although a great deal of language production has taken place before this. Crystal suggests that the babbling period provides an important practice stage in the process of developing speech, but is not the real thing. As babbling dies away, and the phonological system begins to build up, there may be a very remarkable contrast in fluency, and it can appear to parents that their child has stopped talking.

The learning of the sound system of a language begins at around 9 months, although it is not completed until around 7 years of age. By the time the child is 5 years old, most of the phonological system has been acquired, although certain features take longer. People differ in their rate of mastery, and many of the more subtle uses of intonation are not acquired until quite late on.

Grammar

As with the phonological system, Crystal hypothesizes that there are several stages through which children pass in acquiring the grammar of their language.

From around 9 to 18 months the majority of sentences are single-element, for example: 'dada', 'there', 'no', 'gone', 'more'. According to Crystal, it is not possible to analyse them in grammatical terms.

From around 18 months until around 2 years, two-element sentences develop, for example: 'dada there', 'more train', 'where mummy', 'car gone'. It is still difficult to describe this stage in grammatical terms because different meanings can be read into the words used.

Stage three runs from approximately 2 years until $2^1/2$ years, with the development of sentences containing three main elements, such as: 'daddy kick ball', 'that big bag', 'where man gone'. Some children will already have begun to fill out sentences by attaching particles to main words, for example: 'daddy kick a ball'. This is a gradual process which continues into the next stage, in which sentence structure increases to four or more main elements, for example: 'Susie going to town today', 'Where's my mummy's hat gone'. A sentence may contain any number of elements up to the permitted maximum – in English this is usually four or five. Parts of each element may not be fully developed, and children will be heard using grammatical words and endings with varying degrees of consistency.

The next stage, from around 3 to $3^1/2$ years, focuses on the learning of complex sentence structure, and basic patterns of sentence sequence. The use of 'and' to join clauses is particularly noticeable (as I experienced when my 3-year-old niece began a sentence on entering my car for a shopping trip, and was still completing it five miles further along the road!).

During the next year the various grammatical systems become thoroughly acquired, although understanding the full meaning of 'must', 'may', 'should', etc. takes several years longer.

The stage after the age of $4^1/2$ involves learning new structures, and learning to comprehend familiar structures fully. Children often use words that they do not fully understand (as do some adults). After the age of 5 the child begins to learn that there are layers in the interpretation of a sentence. Sentences do not always mean what they seem to mean. This stage can continue to puberty and beyond.

Semantics

Meaning arises from the way in which forms are used in relation to objects, ideas and experiences. It cannot be seen or measured in any simple way, and it is not possible to ask a young child directly what a word or sentence 'means'. Only careful studies of tape recordings and videotapes are likely to establish patterns of semantic function and development.

The most common traditional measure of semantic development is vocabulary growth, but there is disagreement between textbooks as to the extent of variation between children. Estimates range from 2 000 to 10 000 words for a 5-year-old.

Fry (1979) suggested that a 2-year-old may have about 200 different words, a 3-year-old 1 000, and a 4-year-old around 2 000, while Sheriden (1968) avoided the problem after age 2¹/₂ and suggested that an average 3-year-old has a 'large intelligible vocabulary, although speech still shows many infantile phonetic substitutions' (see also Sheriden 1988). Nagy and Herman (1987) argued that, no matter how the task is measured, most children encounter new words by the tens of thousands per year, and learn thousands of them, and that for many children the speech of parents and peers may be the single most significant source of vocabulary growth.

Compare this to the deaf child and some indication is given of the immense handicap that hearing loss can present. Di Carlo (1964) estimated that a 'typical five-year-old deaf child' has approximately 25 words, while Rawlings (1971, cited in Conrad 1979a) showed that in a study in the USA of 22 000 children known to have been born deaf, fewer than half were diagnosed at age 3; and that these children reached school age with little concept of the existence of verbal language, and effectively no experience of it. In another major study of over 13 000 deaf children, by Silverman-Dresner and Guilfoyle (1972, cited in Rodda and Grove 1987), the vocabulary scores of respondents aged 8–17 years were studied using English words known to be familiar to hearing children of a younger (6–11 years) age range. Deaf children aged 8–9 years, on average, recognized only 18 out of the pool of 7 300 words. Scores rapidly increased with age, so that subjects in the 16–17 years group responded correctly to 2 545 (35 per cent) of the test words. Rodda and Grove claim that taking these results at face value suggests that the English vocabulary of deaf pupils at the end of their school career is only equivalent to that of a 6-year-old hearing child. (The reader is referred to Rodda and Grove 1987 for a detailed discussion of the linguistic skills of deaf children.)

The deaf child in a hearing home

The stage at which a child is diagnosed as having a hearing problem is extremely important. The sooner hearing aids can be fitted, the sooner the infant may begin to develop the concept of speech sounds.

Acquisition of hearing aid amplification has been shown to be positively correlated with speech intelligibility of older deaf children (Osberger et al 1986; Markides 1983, 1986; Guinagh and Jester 1981; Schweinhart and Weikart 1980). Markides (1986) found that, if hearing aids were fitted before 6 months of age, speech was significantly superior to all other groups tested.

Yet, apart from a fairly crude check at 6 weeks of age, unless there is a history where deafness is suspected, infants are not routinely tested for hearing until they are between 7 and 9 months of age, as this is the optimum time for performing a distraction test. 'Prior to this age sitting balance, head control and sound localisation ability are imperfect. Beyond ten months the development of object permanence and increasing sociability make the test more difficult' (Hall 1989, p.61). This means that the child is already 9 months of age at the earliest before hearing aids can be fitted.

A deaf child can be difficult to diagnose. Deaf infants initially babble as do hearing children, although it has been found that the babbling development is both qualitatively and quantitatively different from that of normally hearing infants (Crystal 1976; Stoel-Gammon and Otomo 1986; Martin 1983; Kent et al 1987; Mavilya 1971; Oller and Eilers 1988), which can be demonstrated with tape recordings. However, without prior knowledge or experience, few parents are likely to pick up these differences in their child.

Even children known to be at risk of hearing impairment are not always seen very promptly. This is illustrated by the following example, where a mother whose first child had a sensorineural loss reported the following experience with her second child:

> Mary had a brainstem-evoked response test. She was referred at 6 weeks. She had it done when she was 5 months. We are now waiting another two months before they consider fitting hearing aids, yet someone else at the group I go to had a history of deafness, so her second child was fitted by 2 months. You need time to get a child to accept them. I would have thought it would have been better to have them fitted now instead of waiting another two months.

In another instance a child with a history of meningitis failed the health visitor screening test at 7 months, was referred immediately to the county medical officer in the area, was seen at 9 months, but the parents were advised to wait and have the child retested at 11 months. That particular child was well over 1 year of age before diagnosis of a sensorineural loss was confirmed and hearing aids fitted. In this case the child went through three screening procedures before being seen by the audiological physician and finally being diagnosed, although it seemed apparent from the first testing that a hearing loss existed.

Once a diagnosis has been made, parents need time and support in coming to terms psychologically with the hearing loss. Through the process of grieving (see Chapter 1) they are able to reassess and reconstruct their beliefs and fantasies about the child, and the capabilities of that child. According to Moses (1985), if the parent does not generate new dreams that the child can fulfil, then each day the child will be seen as a disappointment and failure in the eyes of the parent, and parental disappointment will be communicated to the child.

Often, messages given by professionals conflict with the needs of the parents. Urgency is implied in terms of speech development, fitting hearing aids, etc., at a time when parents need to come to terms with their feelings. New pressures and responsibilities are heaped on already-existing pressures and responsibilities of parenthood, and parents may become anxious, stressed or overwhelmed: 'An overstressed, overwhelmed parent ends up doing nothing, even while appearing to be intensely involved in doing everything; therefore realistic expectations need to be spelled out, along with an understanding that parents have lives beyond their deaf children' (Moses 1985, p.98).

Parent–child communication

In general, parents want their children to be 'normal', yet deaf children are not normal in terms of speech development. For example, Gregory and Mogford (1981) have shown that hearing children develop their first word some five months earlier than deaf children, and move from one to ten words in about one month, compared to seven months for deaf children (see also Geers et al 1984; Geers and Schick 1988). From a review of the research, Rodda and Grove (1987) observed that: 'the many studies of syntactical abilities ... are unanimous in concluding that prelingually profoundly deaf persons rarely, if ever, attain high levels of proficiency in spoken language structures' (p.165).

Many researchers have found that communication between deaf children and hearing parents is often very limited (for example, Furth 1973; Denmark 1976, 1982; Denmark and Warren 1972; Freeman 1976; Gregory 1976; Evans 1988). In a study of 122 deaf and partially-hearing children under 5 years, without sign language, Gregory (1976) found that 57 per cent relied on gesture, showing and pointing when communicating with their mothers, while Denmark and Warren (1972) observed that the majority of patients referred to their psychiatric unit were young deaf people with problems of behaviour and adjustment, whose parents were only able to communicate with them on a very superficial level.

These findings are not confined to the UK. For example, a comparative study in the Greater Vancouver area of Canada, of all deaf children aged 5–14 years, found that many teenagers still had no communication with their families except at a primitive level, and many of those who could function well on an oral/aural basis were subjected to severe communication strain in social groups (Freeman 1976).

In a national survey on speech intelligibility carried out in the UK, Markides (1983) found that just over 40 per cent of pupils in schools for the deaf fell within the categories of 'functional' or 'socially acceptable' speech. This means that just under 60 per cent had speech that ranged from 'very difficult to follow' to no speech at all. All schools for the hearing-impaired were requested to participate, and 70 per cent of partial-hearing units and 90 per cent of schools responded. This supports earlier research findings (Ives 1976).

Another report, *Childhood Deafness in the European Community* (Martin and

Moore 1979), studied 3 000 8-year-old children. Rather more than half these children had speech which was unintelligible except to their parents, and in 23 per cent of the total, speech was grossly defective or unintelligible even to parents (Martin 1983). In a study of 360 deaf and partially-hearing children in England and Wales, aged 15 to 16^1/$_2$, Conrad (1979a) found that only 10 per cent had speech that was easy to understand; while Evans (1988) found that, when using speech only, less than half of the children and parents studied could understand all or most of what was communicated whereas, with the addition of signing and fingerspelling, over 90 per cent of children and parents understood what was communicated.

Inevitably problems in communication lead to frustration on the part of both parents and child. For example, the father of a profoundly deaf boy explained:

> Frustration. Definite frustration. Not being able to talk. Even a 2-year-old or an 18-month-old can tell you. When he was a little nipper . . . he hit his leg on the coffee table. He couldn't tell me he'd hit his leg. It upset me. He couldn't say 'My leg hurts'. Definitely a problem with frustration.

While the mother of a severely deaf boy remembered:

> He got very frustrated and I was having a lot of, at the beginning, a lot of problems with him because he would come up to me and shake me and say 'Why don't you understand?' because he knew what he was saying. It's just that we were having problems trying to understand what he was saying. I mean, when 'milk' comes out as 'bok', that's very frustrating for him and he actually took me to the fridge and said 'I want that', and luckily he was old enough to put over and know that if he took me to the fridge and showed me what he wanted, I could say 'Aah. Right. OK. You want milk. I'll get you some milk' . . . It was frustrating for me as well. I used to try and stay calm and aloof from it all and not get frustrated.

In turn the frustration builds up, and emotional and behavioural problems may result.

The following example given by the mother of a girl profoundly deafened with a conductive loss, which was successfully treated surgically, illustrates the link between poor communication and behavioural difficulties:

> She had terrible screaming tantrums from frustration. She was 2^1/$_2$. She couldn't put words together. Since they operated the improvement has been dramatic.
>
> After the operation we used to talk to her and she didn't understand what was going on because she didn't know what speech was. Also the traffic noise used to really frighten her. She used to be terrified and cry. Her grommets were taken out at 4^1/$_2$ [years]. She's still behind with her speech but its improving. She's fine now.

This little girl's behaviour began to improve as she became able to communicate effectively. (Her hearing is now within normal limits.)

Research is consistent in showing that emotional and behavioural difficulties in deaf children are higher than in the general population (Altschuler 1974; Rainer et al 1969; Denmark 1966, 1976; Denmark and Eldridge 1969; Denmark and Warren 1972; Denmark et al 1979; Freeman et al 1975; Furth 1973; Graham 1986).[5]

Two early studies by Kendall (1957, cited in Ewing and Ewing 1964; 1960, cited in J. Montgomery 1986) reported (after studying 180 deaf children and 180 hearing children aged from 18 months to 65 months) that more than twice the incidence of temper tantrums occurred among the deaf than the normal-hearing. Also, difficulties over feeding, sleeping, toilet training, fears and aggressiveness were found to be much more common in deaf children, and these tended not to decline with age (although both Kendall and Ewing and Ewing noted that the susceptibility of many deaf children to temper tantrums diminished with language development).

In keeping with other findings, as well as frustration and temper tantrums, bedwetting and sleeping problems were encountered by parents in the present study.

In a study on hearing children, Baker et al (1983) found that children with behavioural problems at an early age were much more likely to have behavioural problems three-and-a-half to four years later than were matched control children. These results confirm the previous work of Richman et al (1975, 1982); Bentovim (1976); and Jenkins et al (1980).

Following the original work of Robertson (1958), an association has been found between hospitalization in early life and later behavioural disorders in normal children (Quinton and Rutter 1976; Bowlby 1989; Kraemer 1989; Mason 1989). Freeman (1977), in an epidemiological study, found that deaf children are far more likely to experience hospitalization than their hearing peers, especially in the first two years of life. This suggests that deaf children are likely to be at much greater risk of developing behavioural disorders, not only from problems within the family but also from other outside influences.

There is evidence to suggest that children with markedly defective speech at 7 years are likely to continue to have difficulties in areas of acceptable verbal communication, social maturity and scholastic achievement (Sheriden and Peckham 1975), and a significant, though weak, relationship has been found between attention problems in childhood and antisocial behaviour eight years later (Wallander 1988). As severely and profoundly deaf children begin their school life with speech problems, and many experience behavioural problems, they may also be in danger of carrying antisocial behaviour into adolescent and adult life unless an adequate means of communication is found.

How hearing parents will communicate with their deaf child appears to be largely a matter of professional advice and opinions (see Chapter 7). The decision as to whether or not the child should learn sign language is surrounded by professional bias, and often practical difficulties. (For example, the author has personal knowledge of a situation where the father changed his job, and the whole family moved several hundred miles in order to achieve a signing education for their child, who had been deafened by meningitis, because no provision was available where they lived.)

By far the majority of hearing parents do not know sign language when their child is diagnosed deaf. Using this method requires the whole family to be involved in learning a foreign language, so communication with the child becomes dependent on a large number of factors, including motivation, willingness and ability of parents to learn sign language, the availability of classes, the degree of hearing impairment, professional advice given, etc. Some of these issues are discussed later.

The deaf child in a deaf home

As discussed in Chapter 1, in contrast to the reaction of hearing parents, deaf parents do not tend to experience the diagnosis of deafness in their child as a crisis, particularly if the household communicates in sign language. Unlike the situation for hearing parents, there is virtually no adjustment for deaf parents to make when their child is diagnosed deaf (Grant 1987), and they are not rendered powerless or helpless by the child (Schlesinger 1985).

Research into language acquisition in the deaf home is of fairly recent origin, with much pioneering work conducted in the USA, but it is now gaining momentum, and studies are being reported worldwide. In the UK there has been a rapid expansion of interest over the past two decades, with several research groups undertaking studies in this field (notably Birkbeck College, University of London; Bristol University; Open University linked with Nottingham University, among others), and publications are increasing.[6]

Studies suggest that the pattern of language acquisition in the deaf home in the first year of life is the same as in the hearing home (Kyle 1988; Caselli 1983, 1987; Petitto 1987; Volterra 1981; Volterra and Caselli 1985; Schlesinger and Meadow 1972). A hearing mother points to an object and says the name of that object. A deaf mother points to an object and models the sign for that object. In both situations the child copies, takes turns, and this leads to conversation.

A study in Japan (Masataka 1992) found that deaf mothers used signs at a significantly slower tempo with their deaf infants than when communicating with deaf adult friends. Also they tended to repeat the same sign frequently, and the movements associated with each sign were somewhat exaggerated, in a similar way to hearing mothers' speech to hearing infants.

In general, signing appears earlier than speech (Bellugi and Klima 1982;

Kyle 1988; Folven and Bonvillian 1991), although Kyle and Woll (1988) have cautioned that problems in analysis can arise because of interpretation of data. Just as hearing parents read meaning into children's utterances, so deaf parents interpret gestures and other body movements which resemble signs as actual early signs.

Both deaf and hearing children use gesture. Gestures co-exist with speech for a long time, and they co-exist with signing for a long time as a normal part of language acquisition (Kyle 1988).

Children develop at different rates. From the families studied by the Bristol research group, one child before the age of 1 year had developed around 35 signs, one had 12 signs, and one had no signs at all until 17 months of age, which shows a similar pattern to hearing children (Kyle 1988). A study by Folven and Bonvillian (1991) reported that, on average, children of deaf parents produced their first recognizable sign at 8.2 months of age, developed ten recognizable signs by 13.5 months and combined signs by 16.1 months. The children did not use the signs to name new objects until a mean age of 12.6 months, after they had demonstrated communicative pointing. The early signs were mainly imitations of parental signs, signs used in interactive routines, and requests for familiar items.

There is now evidence for babbling in sign language (Petitto and Marentette 1991); and also that children show a distinct and consistent hand preference in their signing, beginning with the production of their first word (Bonvillian and Richards 1993).

The language development of deaf children of deaf parents is basically in line with what is expected from hearing children of the same age; and the progress of deaf children of deaf parents is better than the progress of deaf children of hearing parents (Kyle 1988).

One of the main differences emerging from the studies between deaf and hearing parents is that, although hearing mothers use more language, the deaf mother signs when the child is looking at her; whereas Scroggs (1983) found that hearing mothers tended to sit behind the child, or communicate when the child was not looking at them (sometimes exhibiting irritation when the child did not respond). Harris et al (1989) also found that deaf mothers adopted various strategies to enable the child to see both the sign and its context, although a study by Swisher (1992) which looked at deaf parents signing a story from a book found that all the children experienced problems with their need to focus simultaneously on two sources of information – the mother's signs and the picture book.

In the main, deaf mothers were found to sign within the child's pre-existing focus of attention – that is, where the child was already looking – and there is speculation that hearing parents could be introduced to these strategies as a means of improving communication with their deaf children. Gregory and Barlow (1986) have argued that deaf mothers have skills which help the deaf infant to establish prelinguistic skills of joint reference, role-reversal and turn-taking, and concluded that 'we have a great deal to learn from deaf mothers about how to establish good communication with deaf children' (p.18). Also, Harris et al (1989) pointed out that the development of signing strategies is affected by the child as well as the mother, and by the wider context in which signing occurs.

Language acquisition and interactive studies

Over the past two decades there has been an increasing focus on studies of interaction and language acquisition in both hearing and deaf children, and the importance of experience prior to the use of spoken language is becoming apparent as research in this area develops.

Gurney (1973) has identified four conditions which are necessary before a normal-hearing child begins to talk. These include: adequate interpersonal relationships; perceptual and motor maturation (especially auditory listening skills); reward for early attempts at communication, and an adequate level of intelligence. The deaf child immediately loses out in one of these areas, and could do so in all of them.

Adequate interpersonal relationships will depend very much on individual factors within each family setting, although it is well documented that emotional difficulties between parent and child are more common in families with deaf children than with normal-hearing children.

According to Martin (1983) the stages of neuromotor control leading to speech development are different for deaf infants. It is not just that they cannot hear sound, but that they do not gain the same control and coordination of their vocal apparatus as hearing children. They have poor control over respiratory activity because they do not control and repeat sounds as a hearing baby does. To complicate matters there may also be other handicaps present (Markides 1983; Van Uden 1981). (Two handicaps have been identified by Van Uden which specifically affect language acquisition in the deaf child. One involves motor development, and the second is a cognitive-motor handicap.)

Deaf children do not receive auditory reward and reinforcement to the same extent as normal-hearing children, and there is some evidence to suggest that they do not receive the same socio-emotional reward for early attempts at communication as hearing children (for example, Scroggs 1983), although naturally the degree of reward will vary from individual to individual.

Although studies have shown the deaf to have the same distribution of non-verbal intelligence as hearing people (Vernon 1968, 1969), Howarth and

Wood (1977) have hypothesized that deafness interferes with the intellectual development of deaf children because of the devastating effects which poor communication has on the quality of their interaction with others, particularly on parents and teachers. (Watson et al 1982 have suggested that non-verbal intelligence and visual memory skills may be important in understanding the success of some deaf children in acquiring English, and the failure of others.)

Tait (1987) has identified five stages through which deaf children pass in making the transition from preverbal communication to the beginnings of conversational competence. For a normal baby, an essential precursor of understanding and talking is the development of such strategies as turn-taking and shared visual reference (see also Gregory and Mogford 1981; Trevarthen 1974). For the deaf baby, initially there is no awareness of conversation at all. Tait calls this the 'disengaged stage'. At the second stage, the 'engaged stage', the child becomes aware when a person is talking, and looks at the person. Stage three involves structured looking; stage four, structured vocalizations, and in stage five there is an equal conversational partnership between the child and speaker.

Kuczaj (1986) has argued that children must learn the sounds of their language in order to learn to combine them together to produce meaningful words, and then must learn to combine words in sentences in order to communicate more complex meaning, yet a severely or profoundly deaf child is not hearing the sounds from which a vocabulary is eventually built up.

Following diagnosis of deafness, professionals emphasize to hearing parents that they must talk to their deaf child as much as possible in order for that child to hear sounds (Grant 1987; Clark 1983; Courtman-Davies 1979; Nolan and Tucker 1981; Tweedie 1987; Reeves 1976; Watson 1976; Crandell 1978; Wilkinson 1979); yet until the above stages identified by Tait have been reached and passed through, it seems that the deaf child may be unaware of the connection between sound and communication.

Research undertaken on caregiver–child interaction has elicited both the importance of the main caregiver role in influencing language development, and that the infant has the ability to communicate in a variety of ways prior to the acquisition of speech.

'Exchanges' in conversation between caregiver and child have been demonstrated from as early as two months (Trevarthen 1974; Snow 1977), and infants use many rhythmical movements and patterns as strategies to communicate (Tronick et al 1979; Fridman 1980). It has been found that the normal-hearing infant is actively engaged in processing sounds from soon after birth (Panneton Cooper and Aslin 1989); infant vocalizations occur with changes in experience (Hilke 1988), and infant action has an effect on caregiver action (for example, Bell 1971, 1974; Brazelton et al 1974; Bruner

1977; Stern 1977; Collis 1979). When talking to infants, mothers typically use a rising intonation contour to attract attention, and a rising–falling contour to maintain attention (Stern et al 1982; Stern et al 1983). Also, it has been noted that parents read meaning into their babies' actions and responses from birth and very early on (Hastings and Hayes 1981; Reilly et al 1984) and can make a good guess at whether or not the baby is understanding them.

The type of speech encountered by children is an important variable in their learning of language (Lieven 1982) and an increasing number of studies have focused on this aspect. Harris et al (1983, 1984/85) demonstrated a close correspondence between maternal speech to infants and the immediate non-verbal context in which it occurs. In the 1983 study almost all maternal utterances concerned the child's immediate environment, particularly objects on which the child was focusing attention, and actions in which the child was actively engaged. The 1984/85 study revealed significant changes in the way mothers responded to their children at the different ages studied (9 months and 16 months) which reflected the child's increasing comprehension and production skills. They argued that the change in the mother was largely the result of her expectation that the child was on the verge of using words, and that the linking of language to familiar objects and activities by the mother facilitated the child's discovery of connections between words, objects and events (they cite Messer 1983, who has put forward a similar argument).

Several studies have found that children's speech and language acquisition is linked to the kind of maternal speech with which they are presented (de Blauw et al 1979; Halliday and Leslie 1986; Harris et al 1988). Differences have been found between mothers' speech to normal children and disabled children. For example, Beeghly et al (1986) found a significant difference between mothers of normal and Down's syndrome children in the way they used speech. Yet Bellinger (1980) found a striking absence of variability in the speech that mothers used with the same-age non-disabled children. In their study it was also noted that speech changed at certain stages in the child's development. This was interpreted as the mothers responding to changes in the language behaviour of their children. Bellinger found that the age of the child to whom a mother was speaking could be inferred very accurately from her speech. Older siblings also have an effect. Woollett (1986) showed that the presence of older siblings reduced the amount of language spoken by mothers, their responsiveness to the younger children, and the younger children's verbal contribution. Therefore, in a family where the deaf child has older siblings, the amount of time available for parents to participate in language stimulation is likely to be reduced.

There is increasing evidence that speech to children differs from adult-to-adult speech (Snow 1972, 1977, 1979) in ways that appear to facilitate the language acquisition of the child (Bradley and Caldwell 1976; Cross 1977;

Bellinger 1980; Harris et al 1986); and Wood (1982) found that some aspects of adult–child interactions are different for deaf children but that, with suitable intervention, these aspects can be altered to have beneficial effects, especially in an educational setting.

A study by Power et al (1990) compared mothers with normal-hearing and deaf children aged 1–5 years and found that there appeared to be a different role for maternal control over conversation with very young deaf children who are just beginning to speak, and older ones who have developed conversational skills. They argued that the control exerted by mothers was facilitative at early stages, but repressive, just as for hearing children, once deaf children had something to contribute. They also found that maternal power over deaf children's conversation did seem to decline with age to the point where 8-year-old deaf children were being controlled about the same as 5-year-old hearing children.

These findings link to earlier studies by Gross (1970) – who found that mothers of normal-hearing children used more questions and asked for more opinions and suggestions (rather than giving them) than did mothers of deaf children – and Gregory et al (1979) – who argued that, while all the literature on the development of deaf children emphasizes their need for language stimulation, and that notice needs to be taken of their own speech, it would appear that, compared with hearing children, less notice is taken of their utterances and they are talked to less as they get older.

In a pilot investigation of two mother–infant dyads, with a hearing and deaf infant respectively, important differences were found between the dyads (Nienhuys and Tikotin 1983). The deaf infant spent approximately 98.5 per cent of his time in neutral or negative emotional phases, whereas the hearing infant divided his time equally between neutral-to-negative and positive emotional phases. Similarly, the mother of the deaf infant spent over half her time in emotionally neutral behavioural phases, with only 14.6 per cent of time in play, whereas the mother of the hearing infant spent some 54.8 per cent of the time in play. Although this was a pilot study, and the findings could be due to individual differences, Nienhuys and Tikotin suggest that this study exposes a fruitful ground for research with potentially important implications for the management of the newly-diagnosed hearing-impaired infant and his primary caregiver. They argue that 'if professionals seek to create opportunities for the development of maximal communicative competence in the hearing-impaired child, then the early mother–infant interaction, and any adaptations created by infant deafness, ought to be more clearly understood' (Nienhuys and Tikotin 1983, p.191).

It has been found that the first words of the deaf child are deliberately elicited and trained, and that 'the saying of a word in those early stages is an end in itself, rather than part of a transaction within an interaction' (Gregory and Mogford 1981, p.225). According to Rodda and Grove (1987), an important prerequisite to the development of speech is the development of internalized language, and failure to develop these structures reduces speech to a mechanical skill, having no significance for the child as a means of communication. Hence, speech training that is not coupled with an analysis of the child's language skills results merely in parrot-like repetition of sounds.

This finding is supported by the following account, to the author, from a profoundly deaf woman who was deafened by meningitis prelingually:

> The meningitis left me paralysed and with a bad chest. It was a long time before I was able to walk properly. I had no speech, no hearing and I couldn't walk.
> I was forced to lip read. I would say words without understanding them. I didn't understand what they meant. If I didn't say the word right at home I would get no dinner. So I learned to say it right. I got hit by my mother if I didn't say it right but I needed the sign before the speech in order to be able to understand.

Further evidence comes from Furth (1966), who argued that deaf children have been called 'rigid' in their thinking, because they learn to repeat parrot-fashion what has been drilled into them. The situation did not improve for the woman in the above example when she reached the educational system:

> When I started school I spent the first few months sitting on the teacher's lap. She felt sorry for me because I was deaf.
> At the age of 6 I was sent to a boarding school for the deaf. No sign was allowed in the school. We were not allowed to sign in the classroom. I learned to sign with other deaf children. We developed our own sign language – the older children taught the younger ones. We signed in the playground. It was a hard life. It was hell. But I was more happy at school than at home.

This woman had been trained to speak and to lip read, but the words she used had no meaning for her. When she left school she was unable to write, or to understand words she read. She was unable to communicate effectively with hearing people until she was well into adulthood.

Deaf children lose out in many areas. Oshima-Takane (1988) has shown that normal-hearing children under the age of 2 years can attend to, and learn from, speech which is not addressed to them. This means that they are absorbing information even when apparently preoccupied and not obviously attending to the conversation around them. A deaf child is isolated from such information and must concentrate hard on what another person is conveying in order to receive information in an interactive setting. A study of the verbal games of preschool children by Iwamura (1980), which investigated children's acquisition of the rules of grammatical construction and social usage, found that there were three steps used in acquiring these rules. These involved: monitoring one's own and another's speech; providing someone else with appropriate information about what is being said, and responding to what others say about one's own speech. Yet an earlier study by Hoemann (1972) on the development of communication skills in deaf and hearing children suggests that deafness constitutes a handicap in peer-to-peer communication even with manual methods, while Quigley et al (1974) found that the deaf have difficulty in understanding questions put to them. They found that, although results of this study indicated an improvement in comprehension with age, even the youngest hearing children in the study (aged 8 years) obtained higher scores than most of the deaf children (aged 10–19 years). Only with yes/no questions (that is, the theoretically least complex type of question) did the deaf approach the level of comprehension of much younger normal-hearing children.

Watts (1967) has argued that speech supplies the intellectual element which is needed to make the control of feeling possible. As the child's command of speech is extended they begin to realize it is not necessary to resort to temper tantrums to gain ends. Yet the deaf child with poor speech development does not have this outlet. In fact, according to Altschuler (1974), the problem goes beyond actual speech. He has pointed out that for the hearing child, emotion can be evoked and conveyed through sound. At a few weeks of age the normal child can often be quieted by the comforting sound of its mother's voice. Also, other important clues such as tone and volume help the infant to recognize emotion (for example, anger, encouragement, tenderness and love). This is an important part of the child's tie with the mother, and one which the deaf child does not have.

As Altschuler pointed out:

> language has a role in communicating emotion. When such communication is interfered with the bond between parent and child is altered, and along with it the quality of closeness and the clarity of identification of feelings. It is questionable whether later efforts at replacement – even if successful – can make up for the early deficiency in the deaf child. (p.368)

Rodda and Grove (1987) argued that the problem is not in learning speech but in imposing it on deaf children and that, if we teach speech to deaf children in a way that destroys their self-esteem and self-identity, and in a way that attacks the role models provided by successful deaf people, we will deprive deaf children of experiences that are vital to their educational development. Education of the deaf child is discussed in the next chapter.

Notes

1   See also Laing (1959; 1961; 1967); and Laing and Esterton (1970).
2   For further reading regarding the development of the concept of mental illness in sociological terms, see Szasz (1972); Scheff (1967); Goffman (1974; Rosenhan (1973); and for a perspective of European socio-economic and cultural history, Foucault (1971).
3   Evidence for sign being an indigenous language is cited in Rodda and Grove (1987, p.296), who argue that: 'Perhaps one of the most extraordinary findings of recent years is the discovery that deaf infants are capable of formulating an elementary form of sign language spontaneously' (and they cite Goldwin-Meadow and Feldman 1975, 1977; Kuschel 1973 and Mohay 1982 for evidence). They argue that:

The children in these studies do not, it seems, copy their mothers' informal gestures. Mostly they invent their own novel iconic symbols and incorporate them in multisign discourse ... This research, if confirmed, provides powerful evidence for the existence of an innate communication mechanism capable of creating, as well as assimilating, a sign language system.

See also Acredolo and Goodwyn (1988).
4   See Crystal (1976) for a full description of language acquisition.
5   See Rodda and Grove (1987) for a detailed discussion of some of the studies undertaken.
6   For an overview of sign language studies see Kyle and Woll (1988); and Rodda and Grove (1987).

4 Education and deaf children

The past two decades have seen a gradual shift of emphasis in deaf education away from a strictly oral/aural approach, through Signed English and Total Communication, towards bilingualism using British Sign Language (BSL) with English as a second language. At the same time the trend towards integrating children with special needs into ordinary schools has increased steadily.

Education facilities for deaf children vary enormously and, although the emphasis is changing, many of the issues are far from settled. The type of communication method to be used, and where deaf children should be educated (in ordinary schools, or separately in special schools and units), remain controversial issues which have their roots in the very beginnings of deaf education.

Historical perspective

According to Hodgson (1953), until the seventeenth century, when technology advanced understanding of the nature of sound, the attitude towards deafness was one of fatalism.[1] The view Aristotle (384–322 BC) put forward – that the deaf could not learn to speak because their tongues were tied, and 'those who are born deaf all become senseless and incapable of reason' (Hodgson 1953, p.62) – lasted for more than 2 000 years. Deaf people became outcasts and were ill-treated.

The earliest legislation to protect the deaf came from Hebrew law, where discrimination was made between categories of deafness. People deaf and dumb from birth were completely without rights or obligations and were required to have legal guardians. They were not allowed to marry.

Hodgson found evidence that the deaf developed a language of their own at a very early date. He cites a reference by Plato (*c.* 428–*c.* 348 BC) in the *Cratylus*, where Socrates (469–399 BC) remarked: 'If we had no voice or tongue, and wished to make things clear to one another, should we not try, as dumb people actually do, to make signs with our hands, and head and person generally?' (Hodgson 1953, p.73). Some thousand years later, St Augustine (d. 604) also mentioned a deaf man who understood others by their gestures. Yet, although sign language existed among both deaf and hearing people who had certain uses for it, its potential for education was not explored prior to the sixteenth century.

During the sixteenth century an Italian mathematician and physician, Girolamo Cardano, developed a scheme for teaching the deaf to read, which marked a turning point in the attitude towards deafness, although there is no evidence that it was actually taught.

The real pioneer in deaf education was Pedro Ponce de León (1520–1584), a Spanish Benedictine monk, whose main aim was to teach speech to his deaf pupils in order for them to achieve oral prayer and confession. He taught reading and writing and developed a sign system between teacher and pupil. All his pupils were young men of noble families who were heirs to great estates. Because under Roman law deaf mutes were unable to inherit, the families had economic and legal motives for wanting their sons to speak.

The seventeenth century brought changes in educational thought, and the first teachers of the deaf. Some major influences in educational reform in England were John Locke (1632–1704), who helped to alter English attitudes away from ill-treatment of the deaf, and George Dalgarno (*c.* 1626–1687), who laid the foundations for deaf education, and in Spain, Juan Pablo Bonet, who was the first to use lip reading for a pupil.

The first known English teachers of the deaf were Dr John Wallis (1616–1703) and Dr. William Holder. Wallis was asked to undertake the education of Daniel Whalley, who had been deaf since 5 years of age, while Holder undertook to teach Alexander Popham, a congenitally deaf 10-year-old, to speak. After three years scant progress had been made, and Holder was regarded as having failed. Popham was sent to Wallis, and a feud began between the two men.

This quarrel would seem to mark the very beginnings of the present-day controversy in deaf education, and highlights the differences in diagnosis and individual characteristics. Popham was congenitally deaf, without prior knowledge of language, whereas Whalley had been deafened at the age of 5 years, after speech had developed. As deafness was not understood at this time, and the significance of degrees of hearing loss and differences in onset unthought of, it was naturally assumed that one teaching method was superior to the other.

The most famous of all teachers was Charles Michel, Abbé de l'Epée, a

French priest who established the first public school for deaf children in Paris in 1755, teaching up to sixty children with sign language and maintaining them out of his own pocket. In contrast to the secrecy of others at the time, l'Epée published an account of his methods, and was followed by his successor, the Abbé Roch Ambroise Cucurron Sicard, who compiled the first dictionary of signs.

Throughout the nineteenth century schools in Britain increased from one to fifty, and the foundations were laid for the amplification of sound. At the same time, support for charity declined and state aid was not forthcoming. Teachers' salaries were reduced to a pittance and schools struggled to remain solvent. The first Education Bill for hearing children in 1868 made conditions for deaf schools relatively worse.

In 1870 Mr (later Sir) William St John Wheelhouse introduced his bill for the Education of the Deaf, although it had no chance whatsoever of being passed. He continued to introduce it once a year as a gesture.

The growing enthusiasm in Europe for teaching speech brought about the first International Conference of Teachers of the Deaf in Paris in 1878, followed in September 1880 by an international conference in Milan in which members strongly endorsed the use of oral approaches in education and urged that deaf education should follow as closely as possible the methods used for hearing children. They also unanimously carried a resolution demanding state aid for deaf education. Following this conference most countries were swift to adopt oral methods (Schmitt 1966).

A Royal Commission was appointed in 1885, initially confined to the blind, but in 1886 it was extended to include the deaf, and its members were changed to include two pro-oralists and two pro-signers so that no unanimity was reached on methods of educating the deaf (Pritchard 1970). According to Ritchie (1930, cited in Pritchard, p.95) this commission was 'unfortunate in that it gave state recognition to the vicious bracketing of blind with deaf' – a concept which still exists today, even though the needs of the two groups are very different.

In 1893 the Education (Blind and Deaf Children) Act came into being and became operative on 1 January 1894, making education of the deaf free and compulsory.

Twentieth century

The system of deaf education remained quite separate from that of hearing children until the Education Act 1944 (Wright 1969). Since the Second World War, advances in technology and engineering have enabled major improvements in both the diagnosis of hearing impairment and in hearing aids, so enabling more children to be classified as 'hard of hearing' rather than 'deaf' (Montgomery 1976). By 1955 provision for deaf and partially-hearing children had expanded rapidly, although it was directed towards special schools (HMSO 1978, 2.50).

The Chronically Sick and Disabled Persons Act 1970, Sections 25–27, required local authorities, so far as was practicable, to provide for the education of deaf/blind children in maintained or assisted schools, and wanted an increasing number in ordinary schools (HMSO 1978, 2.83). This trend continued with the Education Act 1976, which amended the 1944 Act. It required local authorities to make provision for the education of handicapped pupils in ordinary schools as well as in special schools. Section 10 of this Act would have required local authorities to educate all handicapped pupils in county and voluntary schools, except where this was impracticable. This was not brought into force, and was repealed under Schedule 4 of the Education Act 1981.

In 1973 a Committee of Inquiry was set up to look into the education of handicapped children and young people, under the chairmanship of Mrs Mary Warnock. Following this inquiry the Warnock Report was published in 1978. This provided an overview of existing provisions and made proposals for future policy. The Education Act 1981 was based largely on the proposals of this report.

The Warnock Report was responsible for the change in terminology from 'deaf' to 'hearing-impaired'. Prior to this, in the USA, Vernon (1976) claimed that such terminology is 'harsh and cruel because it blurs the distinction between the reality, and the wishes and fantasies surrounding that reality'. He argued that it tends to imply to parents that the child is something he is not, and can lead to grossly inappropriate educational and rehabilitation approaches (p.106), while in the UK Montgomery (1986b) argued that 'to lump all kinds of hearing loss under the title of "Hearing Impairment" is a verbal blanket generalisation which paves the way for a single overall blanket treatment' (p.56).

Montgomery (1981b) has also pointed out that the Warnock Report did not even mention sign language, although it discussed provision for minority languages for hearing children, and that this was reflected in the Education Act 1981, Section 5(v), in which a child 'belonging to a linguistic minority, unless the child suffers from hearing difficulty not arising from problems with language of instruction', is not considered to have special needs.

With the implementation of the Education Reform Act 1988, and the introduction from September 1989 of a National Curriculum in all state schools, new concerns have been raised about the education of deaf children, with a growing movement of professionals and parents calling for profoundly deaf children to be educated bilingually (with British Sign Language as a first language, and English as a second language) and therefore to come under the bilingual section of the Act rather than under the special needs section as at present (for example, Davis 1989; Fletcher 1987;

Llewellyn-Jones 1987; Daunt 1990; Baker and Brearley 1989; Crawford and Keir 1989; Brennan 1989).

The question of bilingualism in deaf education is discussed in more detail later in this chapter.

Communication in deaf education

Debates regarding which mode of communication should be used with deaf children for teaching purposes are deeply entrenched in the history of deaf education. Although the arguments are less intense than a decade ago, the oral/manual controversy has not yet ended. Following the Milan Conference of 1880 which promoted oralism in deaf educational policy, it took until 1984 for the National Executive Council of the British Association of Teachers of the Deaf to formally accept Total Communication as a method of education available to deaf children (J. Montgomery 1986); and, according to Woodford (1987), 'debates about the use of sign language have moved from total rejection to controlled acceptance' (p.167).

Two opposing views are expressed within the oral/manual debate, with one extreme advocating oral/aural methods only, and the other arguing totally for sign language without the use of any form of oral/aural input. Although these two views are diametrically opposed, similar principles are recommended for each (Holsgrove 1987).

The extreme oralist argument suggests that if deaf children learn to use sign language or gesture they will fall back on this easier method of communication and never learn to speak. Without speech they will be unable to communicate with hearing people, and so will be unable to live full lives in the hearing community. At the other end of the spectrum are exponents who recognize British Sign Language (BSL) as a fundamental aspect of deaf culture, and within that culture the deaf do not need speech. The majority of professionals fall somewhere on a continuum between these two views, tending more towards one side than the other.

A national survey of all schools for the deaf and partial-hearing in the UK in the 1980–81 school year showed a trend away from oral methods to Total Communication increasing in schools, although in partial-hearing units the overwhelming majority use oral methods (Jordan 1981, 1986). A follow-up study (which looked only at schools for the deaf) suggested that, within the Total Communication philosophical framework the role of Signed English was being restricted to English-language activities, whereas Signs-Supporting English was used for general communication purposes. There was also an increasing interest in BSL, but a lack of clarity about its educational role, particularly in the teaching of English language skills (Baker and Child 1993).

The oral/manual controversy was at its height during the 1970s.[2] Since then, following the work of Conrad (1979a, 1981), who surveyed all deaf UK school leavers in 1977 and found the average reading age of profoundly deaf 16-year-olds to be 8 years, and the realization that BSL was a true language in its own right, studies in this field have flourished.

Research has highlighted the poor academic achievement of deaf pupils compared to their hearing peers, both in the UK (for example, Conrad 1979a, 1981; Wood et al 1986; Rodda and Grove 1987) and abroad (Di Francesca 1972; Vernon 1981; Quigley and Paul 1984), and has shown that some profoundly deaf children leave school unable to communicate effectively at all (see Chapter 3). This has led to the questioning of educational methods regarding both teaching methods and communication.

Underlying the oral/aural approach is the firm belief that deaf children have the same basic language-learning capacity as normal-hearing children, and that appropriate hearing aids are now available for all deaf children (Clark 1983). However, Bishop (1983) found indications that the language comprehension of deaf children was deviant as well as delayed, and that deaf children adopt systematic strategies for decoding sentences which are not found in hearing children. Similar findings are reported by Tucker and Nolan (1984), and Holsgrove (1987), whose results also indicated that language problems may sometimes be concealed by the children's use of 'survival strategies' (such as were found in the Meyerson Experiment – see pages 114–115), where sometimes inappropriate responses were given in trying to keep up a pretence of understanding a conversation. Also, Montgomery (1976) has argued that there will always be a hard core of profoundly deaf children to whom the most powerful hearing aid will convey little or nothing.

One of the reasons that the oralist movement has remained so strong has come from normal-hearing parents. Historically this was for legal reasons, as without speech a person could not inherit (Hodgson 1953). Today it is natural for parents to want their child to be the same as themselves. Hearing parents have a hearing model on which to base their conceptions, and the oralist arguments sound very reasonable and appealing.

It is easy for someone to shut their eyes and imagine what it must be like to be blind. It is much harder to understand what deafness must be like. If people put plugs in their ears they may still hear similar sound, although fainter. They do not hear distortions of sound or suffer from tinnitus in the way that deaf people may. Once language has developed it is almost inconceivable to imagine what it must be like not to have it. Spoken language forms such an integral part of the normal-hearing person. It is the fundamental route through which we link our thoughts, actions and deeds to the outside world. Even an adult deafened after speech has developed does not lose the ability to read and write, or to think in words.

It is also a basic misconception that hearing aids will improve the hearing of a deaf person in the same way that spectacles can improve vision. Hearing aids will make good the loss of sound intensity, but will not restore the loss of discrimination in the ear itself (Martin and Grover 1986). Until these things are explained to them, many hearing parents, with no prior knowledge of deafness and its problems, will be only too willing to take the advice of oralists.

For the present study, a statement regarding attitudes towards blindness and deafness was included in the questionnaire, and the results confirmed that the majority of people consider blindness to be a worse affliction than deafness (see Figure 4.1).

Teachers of the deaf were the only group tested who considered deafness (32 per cent) to be worse than blindness (15 per cent), although over half the sample (52 per cent) remained non-committal. In all other groups there was a marked bias towards viewing blindness as worse than deafness. This was greatest among the general public (69 per cent), while the other groups ranged between 42 per cent and 44 per cent.

The next highest category to suggest that deafness was the worse handicap were parents of not-yet-tested children (see the Appendix for details of the survey groups), although only 26 per cent agreed, compared with 42 per cent who thought that blindness was worse. This may be because their children were soon to have their hearing tested, and so these parents would be more aware that hearing impairment could cause problems for the child.

Another reason that normal-hearing parents may shy away from manual methods of communication is because of concern that their child may join the deaf community, resulting in a cultural split within the family. Very few hearing parents are likely to join the deaf community, whereas their deaf children may well do so. (This is discussed further in Chapter 5.)

Sign languages are now accepted as complex linguistic systems with communities of users, sharing universal properties with spoken languages (Woll 1987), and there is now ample evidence to show the improved performance of deaf children who use sign language compared with those who do not.[3]

In order to ascertain attitudes towards sign language, the statement 'Children should be taught sign language in schools so that they can talk to deaf people' was included in the questionnaire.

Very few respondents in any of the groups disagreed with the statement, and none of the pupils in the school with profoundly deaf peers disagreed (see Figure 4.2).

It was expected that the Signing Experience (SE) group would score high in agreement because of their exposure to sign language with their peers, although the 100 per cent agreement response was a little surprising. It was

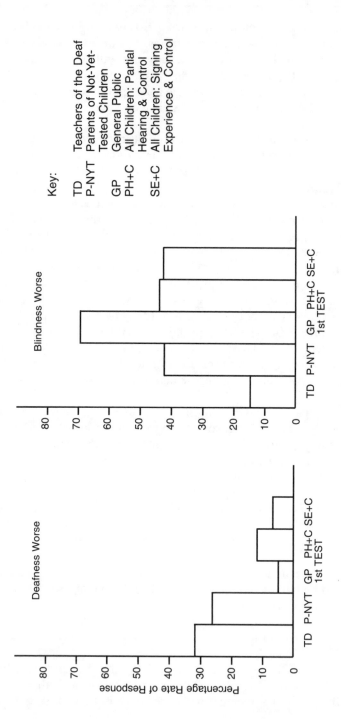

Figure 4.1 Responses of attitudes towards deafness and blindness

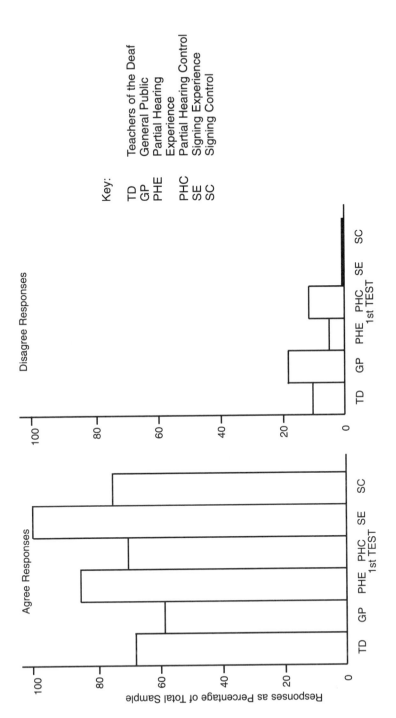

Figure 4.2 Agree/disagree responses to the statement: 'Children should be taught sign language in schools so that they can talk to deaf people'

not expected that the agreement response rate would be so high in the other groups – Signing Control (SC) 76 per cent, Partial Hearing Experience (PHE) 85 per cent, and Partial Hearing Control (PHC) 70 per cent. The agreement response rate was also high in the other groups tested. Of the teachers of the deaf, 67 per cent agreed with the statement although this was a biased sample. Because of recent policy changes, the majority of the teachers tested (82 per cent) were learning some form of sign language. Only 3 per cent of the general public had learned any form of sign language. Of the general public, 54 per cent answered that they knew someone who was deaf. They believed that, of these deaf people, only 9 per cent knew sign language. Yet, despite this limited experience of sign language, 59 per cent of the general public also agreed with the statement. This would suggest that the general public see sign language as having importance and value for communicating with deaf people.

By the end of the school year slight differences were found between the responses in the two schools. The number of agree responses had risen in the SC group to 91 per cent, while in both the PHE and PC groups, although still high, the number had fallen to 70 per cent (see Figure 4.3).

This may well reflect the experience of the pupils in the two schools. The deaf child in the PHE class did not require any form of manual communication, and managed very well in the open classroom situation with the help of a Phonic Ear hearing aid (see page 173), whereas the profoundly deaf pupils in the SE class relied heavily on sign language and fingerspelling for their communication.[4] Also, sign language classes were offered to all pupils at the school who had signing peers in that year (not just in their class), and by the end of the academic year a total of 57 per cent of those tested in the SC group and 68 per cent in the SE group had learned some sign language.

The deaf signers in the school surveyed were using Signed English. Signed English provides a manual means of communication which is easily understood by hearing people and conforms to the required specifications for examinations under our present educational system. Because Signed English is in English word order, theoretically it should be easier for hearing parents to learn than BSL, which is a conceptually different language. However, pressure is now mounting for BSL to be recognized as a language educationally, and for deaf children to be treated as bilingual, with English as a second language.

Fletcher (1987) has argued that the emphasis in English is put on words by stress and intonation – for example, 'Where's the car?' – and that normal-hearing babies can pick out the important word from a sentence just from the tone of voice. Deaf babies do not have this opportunity. She advocates the use of BSL with young deaf children because its structure is far better suited to the deaf infant's mental processes.

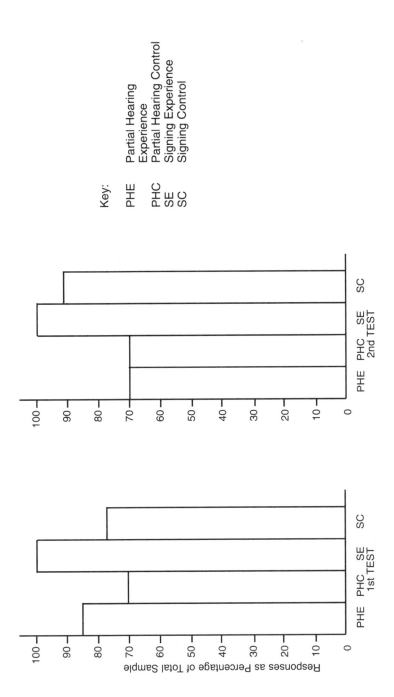

Figure 4.3 Comparison of agree responses between school children (1st and 2nd tests) to the statement: 'Children should be taught sign language in schools so that they can talk to deaf people'

A bilingual child is defined as one who is learning and using two languages (one of which is the mother tongue) irrespective of level of achievement in the languages at any given point (Fitouri 1983). Panou and Sewell (1981) have argued that the deaf constitute a bilingual group, given their exposure to vocal/aural and sign language. They suggest that 'if one accepts the definition of bilingualism which involves alternate use of two languages, then the deaf do constitute such a group, despite an apparent linguistic deficiency' (p.50).

According to Stewart (1984) the deaf represent an ethnic minority who should be able to rightfully demand an education in their own language, while Ladd (cited in Montgomery 1981a, p.434) has asserted that 'rarely in human history has any group of people's views been so ignored as the Deaf view of education'.

A parallel can be drawn between the educational history of the Welsh and (Scottish) Gaelic languages and BSL. Stephens (1976) has documented the repression of Welsh and Gaelic, both through legal enactment and through the education system, which countenanced the humiliating punishment of children for speaking their mother tongue. The education system has been the major channel through which standard English has been steadfastly promoted, and regional and social dialects discriminated against (Rosen 1980).

Currently, over 10 000 children receive instruction in or through the medium of Gaelic in the Scottish education system (MacKinnon and Densham 1989), while in Wales, in 1988, some 169 000 – 66 per cent of the children in the schools of Wales – had some element of Welsh language education (DES/Welsh Office, 1988).

In their survey of schools for the deaf, Baker and Child (1993) found an increasing interest in BSL, but a lack of clarity about its educational role, particularly in the teaching of English language skills, although most schools in the study called for training opportunities for their teachers.

Gradually a realization of the benefits of using deaf adults in schools as role models and communication resources is beginning to re-emerge (following their removal after the Milan Conference of 1880) (Wood 1987, 1988; Daunt 1990), and Woodford (1987) has suggested using the expertise gathered by those who teach English as a second language, when considering the education of deaf children.

Although changes are slowly taking place in deaf education, the UK is still lagging behind many other European countries in this respect (Llewellyn-Jones 1987; Hansen 1987).

Llewellyn-Jones (1987) has argued that, until recently, the education of the deaf has focused on problems and areas of weakness; and that we should be moving towards a system where children's talents and strengths are harnessed. Bilingualism involves normal-hearing and deaf people working together as a team; through sign language the deaf child gets knowledge and advice, learns values and standards, develops socially and emotionally and learns how to express feelings, and there is 'a growing awareness that bilingualism is the way forward in deaf education' (p.27).

Mainstreaming

The trend towards integrating deaf children into mainstream schooling has increased steadily throughout the second half of the twentieth century, and expanded following the Warnock Report (1978) and the Education Act 1981, but present distribution statistics are very difficult to come by in the UK (Markides 1989). The best estimate is that nearly 35 000 hearing-impaired children are receiving some specialized educational tuition. Of these, 80 per cent are in ordinary classes in mainstream education, 12 per cent are in special units attached to ordinary schools and 8 per cent are in special schools for the deaf and/or partial-hearing.

Holsgrove (1987) has argued that the literature takes for granted that integration is highly desirable and advantageous, although he has found that this is not necessarily the case. Implicit in the idea of mainstreaming is the assumption that deaf children will model themselves on hearing children and adjust to a 'normal' lifestyle. By mixing with hearing people they will assimilate the language, values and culture of hearing people so that eventually they will become fully integrated members of the wider normal-hearing society. Without mainstreaming, they remain isolated and segregated, and are deprived of a 'normal' environment.

There is an assumption that handicapped children need experience with normally developing peers, and that this is essential for 'normal' socialization (Ladd et al 1984). But not everyone considers mainstreaming to be of benefit to very deaf children.

For example, Dimmock (1981) cited a 'catastrophic run of events' that occurred in British Columbia, Canada, where a school for the deaf was closed, against protests from the deaf, parents and teachers, and the pupils transferred into mainstream schooling. After ten years, educational attainments in reading, writing and spelling of a number of the pupils were so low that the school had to be re-opened. Dimmock pointed out that, although the school was improved and expanded to deal with the reversed flow of children coming back from mainstream schooling, the victims of the blunder may never be able to read or write for the rest of their lives. From this experience the authorities realized with humility that deaf children have a unique handicap. They need centralization of educational resources and highly trained teaching personnel.

Stewart (1984) has argued that education is dependent upon interaction between the teacher and the pupil, and pupils with their peers. When the communication pathway is blocked, learning suffers. Therefore integration must have a purpose. There needs to be meaningful interaction in order for integration to be successful; so, while it may be appropriate for the hard of hearing, depending on their oral skills, it is much less likely to be appropriate for deaf children, and the most appropriate educational setting depends on the individual.

The sample groups in the present study were investigated for attitudes towards the integration of deaf children in school. With the statement 'Deaf children should go to ordinary schools' there was a mixed response among the various groups tested. Teachers of the deaf were the least in favour: only 23 per cent agreed while 38 per cent disagreed (see Figure 4.4), although 39 per cent remained non-committal.

At the beginning of the school year there was a marked difference between the children in the Signing Experience (SE) group compared with the other classes: 78 per cent agreed with the statement, compared with 46 per cent in the Partial Hearing Experience (PHE) group, 31 per cent in the Partial Hearing Control (PHC) group, and only 24 per cent in the Signing Control (SC) class (see Figure 4.5). By the end of the school year the picture had altered. The number of children who agreed with the statement in the SE group had dropped to 50 per cent, whereas it had risen in all the other classes. Now the group most in favour of deaf children being educated in ordinary schools was the PHE group with 61 per cent, closely followed by the PHC group (58 per cent). There was a smaller rise in the SC class to 30 per cent.

These results may reflect the different experience of the groups. The child in the PHE group was fully integrated into the class, whereas the profoundly deaf pupils, known to the SE group, relied heavily on sign language and the help of interpreters, and only joined the class for certain activities. It would seem that by the end of the school year it was becoming apparent to some children in the SE group that ordinary schools might not always be the best place for deaf children, and the non-committal category trebled from 12 per cent to 36 per cent in this group.

The arguments concerning mainstreaming are in some ways very similar to those regarding modes of communication. On a common sense level it seems both logical and beneficial to mix normal-hearing and deaf children together so that they both benefit from each other, in the same way that it is argued that deaf children are bound to speak if they mix with hearing children. It is only when these issues are studied at a deeper level that the disadvantages begin to appear.

Educational provision for the blind and the hearing-impaired have been linked together historically for over a hundred years (since 1886), yet the needs of the two groups are very different.

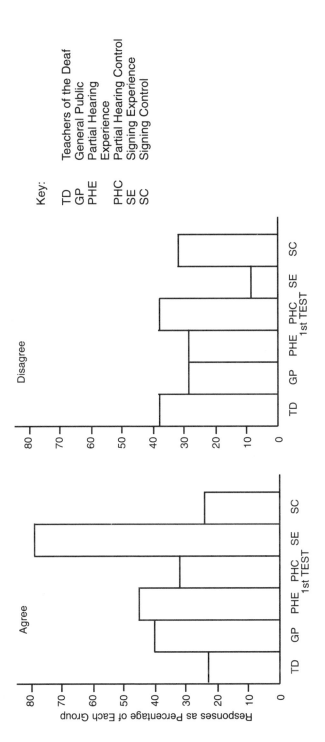

Figure 4.4   Agree/disagree responses to the statement: 'Deaf children should go to ordinary schools'

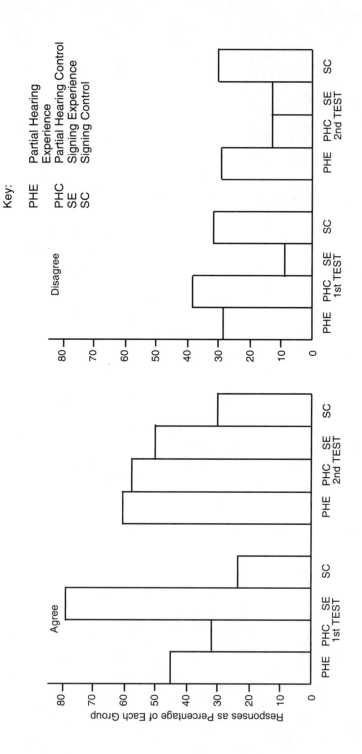

Figure 4.5 Agree/disagree responses of school children (1st and 2nd tests) to the statement: 'Deaf children should go to ordinary schools'

Significant differences were found between the teachers of the deaf and all other groups tested with the statement 'Deaf children and blind children need to learn in different ways, but they should be taught together in the same schools.' Only 8 per cent of the teachers agreed with this statement, while 84 per cent disagreed. The highest 'agree' response came from the PHE group (58 per cent) followed by the PHC (36 per cent), SC group (32 per cent), the general public (22 per cent) and then the SE group (21 per cent) (see Figure 4.6).

The teachers of the deaf, with their knowledge and experience, were very definitely not in favour of the integration of these two groups of pupils with special needs. The children in the PHE group were most in favour, presumably because their experience of integration was positive, while the SE group were the least in favour out of the other groups tested. This may reflect a greater awareness, through their contact with profoundly deaf peers, of the difficulties encountered by pupils with special needs who have more than a marginal disability.

Many deaf children also have additional disabilities. A national survey in the UK found that over 30 per cent of children in schools for the deaf had additional handicaps (which were mainly visual problems and mental retardation), and in some schools the proportion was as high as 70 per cent (Markides 1983). So some children with both deafness and visual disorders are being taught in the same schools as those with only a hearing impairment. With the current trend towards mainstreaming increasing, more children are finding their way into ordinary classrooms, and some profoundly deaf children are being placed in partial-hearing units rather than special schools (Jordan 1981), so there is a risk that the very different special needs of these children may not be fully catered for.

Children spend a large proportion of their lives in school. If they are unhappy in their educational environment they are likely to suffer socially and emotionally.

Two early studies by Johnson (1962) and Fisher (1965) (cited in Morris 1981, p.265) investigated the emotional stability and social adjustment of deaf children placed in ordinary classes. Both studies showed that approximately half the pupils studied (47 per cent) had unsettled or maladjusted behaviour.

In order to benefit from mainstreaming, deaf children need to be accepted by their hearing peers. However, a study by Moss (1987) in the UK found that deaf children were less accepted as they progressed through the school. In a study of speech intelligibility, friendship and associations of hearing-impaired children in secondary schools, Markides (1989) found that 51 per cent of hearing-impaired children considered another hearing-impaired child to be their best friend, and 27 per cent considered a hearing child to be their best friend (22 per cent of deaf, and 12 per cent of hearing children did

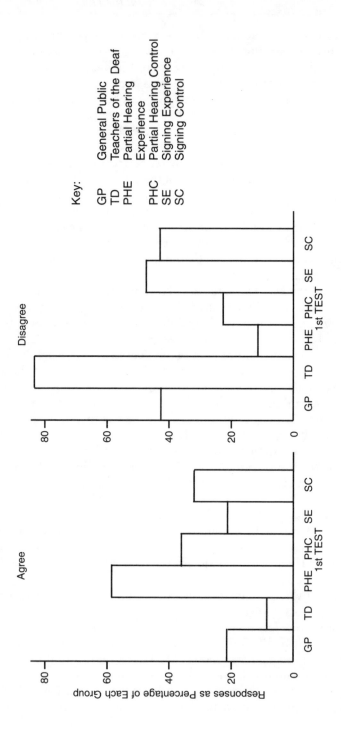

Figure 4.6 Agree/disagree responses to the statement: 'Deaf children and blind children need to learn in different ways, but they should be taught together in the same schools'

not consider anyone at school to be their best friend). Only 3 per cent (5 out of 192) of hearing children considered a hearing-impaired child to be their best friend. One of the main difficulties related to oral communication. When speech was rated on a point scale (1 = normal, 2 = very easy to follow, 3 = fairly easy to follow, 4 = rather difficult to follow, 5 = very difficult to follow, 6 = unintelligible), mainstream teachers and hearing children assigned only 28 per cent–36 per cent of hearing-impaired children to the top three categories.

Lewis and Lewis (1987) have found that even 6- and 7-year-old children have already developed attitudes towards their handicapped peers after only brief involvement with them; and it has been shown in several studies that hearing preschoolers reject the attempts of deaf children to communicate (for example, Vandell et al 1982; Vandell and George 1981) or they remain separate from them (Lindsay and Dickinson 1987; Levy-Schiff and Hoffman 1985).

Results of a survey in the USA of 2 392 children on their attitudes towards handicapped peers (Voeltz 1980) suggested that it may be possible to modify attitudes, and that interventions need to be developed to facilitate social acceptance of individual differences in integrated school settings.

The attitudes of peers towards their deaf classmates is vitally important, but of equal importance is the attitude of the professionals, particularly the teaching staff. Voeltz (1980) has argued that the attitudes of normal children towards disabled peers are affected by adults with whom they have contact. If children develop their attitudes from adults, then the attitude of teachers is likely to have a profound effect on the integration of disabled pupils into mainstream classes.

The Warnock Report (1978) identified positive attitudes of personnel towards integration as a crucial factor in the success of mainstreaming programmes. However, Center and Ward (1987) found that there was resistance by headteachers towards the mainstreaming of all disabled children other than those with mild retardation and sensory handicaps. More recently an evaluation of two large studies (Ward and Center 1987) indicated that, although most teachers are supportive of the policy of mainstreaming, they feel underqualified and too overworked to cope with integration.

A study by Thomas (1985) also reported negative attitudes among teachers towards the integration of intellectually disabled children. Although profoundly deaf children in general are not intellectually disabled (Vernon 1968), because of their communication difficulties they are generally well behind their hearing peers in their schooling (Conrad 1979a) and so are likely to present problems for the class teacher in trying to keep them up to the same standards as their hearing peers. Should the deaf child be given extra time to the detriment of the hearing majority, or should the rest of the class proceed normally and let the deaf child sink deeper and deeper into a pit of confusion, frustration and isolation?

An attempt was made to ascertain whether or not people were aware of the low level of achievement of deaf pupils in schools, with the statement 'Deaf children will do worse in exams than hearing children, except in exams where they don't have to use words.'

A significant difference was found between teachers of the deaf and the general public with this statement: 64 per cent of teachers agreed with the statement, compared with only 24 per cent of the general public. Conversely, 62 per cent of the public disagreed, compared with only 30 per cent of the teachers (see Figure 4.7).

As expected, many of the school children gave a non-committal response (PHC 58 per cent, PHE 50 per cent, SE 36 per cent, SC 33 per cent). However, of those who did respond, it was interesting to note that 38 per cent of the SE group agreed with the statement, whereas 52 per cent of the SC group disagreed.

From these findings it would appear that, in general, people are not aware of the disadvantages deaf children face in examination situations, compared with their hearing peers, unless those people have knowledge of the deaf. The teachers of the deaf had specialist knowledge, while those in the SE class had met profoundly deaf children and so were more aware of their limitations in spoken language.

These findings may have important implications in view of the UK government's decision to publish examination results and league tables for schools. Such figures can give a false impression to members of the public who are unaware of the problems deaf children face. In general, parents want the best education for their child, and the government has emphasized the importance of parental choice in education, but these tables could be a two-edged sword for children with learning difficulties. Parents may shy away from specialist schools (which may be the best educational setting for their child) because of their apparently poor educational attainment record and low place in the tables, while some schools may refuse to take deaf children (and other children with learning difficulties) who could benefit from integration, because of a fear of lowering their place in the tables.

According to Gregory and Bishop (1989), the goals of integration are: the fostering of social integration; the provision of a natural language environment, and the provision of a wider curriculum; but these goals are not being met. They found that often the deaf child does not have the competence in spoken language to benefit from the orally presented wider curriculum of the mainstream school, and that exposure does not necessarily imply access.

Various surveys and studies undertaken on integration have produced similar results. Markides (1989) concluded that, in the UK, 'hearing-

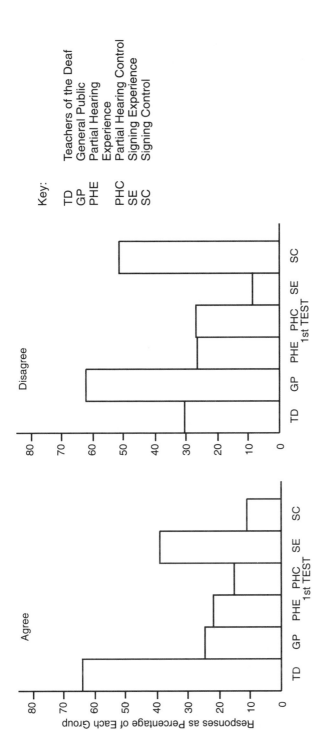

Figure 4.7 Agree/disagree responses to the statement: 'Deaf children will do worse in exams than hearing children, except in exams where they don't have to use words'

impaired children are the most mainstreamed of all handicapped children, but as yet they have not received the degree of special help they need' (p.71); while Holsgrove (1987) has argued that total integration based on access to a common curriculum is not a realistic aim at present, and recommended the need for a flexible response to educational placements, supported by teachers with appropriate specialist training and experience. Mere contact between handicapped and non-handicapped pupils does not indicate integration (Moss 1987), and the deaf child does not experience 'normal' education simply by being placed in a mainstream class (Gregory and Bishop 1989). According to Garretson (1981) there is concern that the child is being dehumanized into a piece of movable data, because mainstreaming has become an end in itself.

Many authors have called for a multidisciplinary approach, both to integration and to the education of the deaf in general (for example, Tait 1987; Morris 1981; Wood et al 1986), for social and emotional factors to be taken into consideration as well as the level of deafness (Reed 1981), and also that the method should be suited to the child, not the child to the method (Sheavyn 1976). It is important to ascertain which children will benefit from integration (Morris 1981), although 'there is a major lack of equipment for use in assessing or predicting achievement with deaf children, although research is being done in this area' (Powell et al 1985, p.13).

Musselman et al (1988) drew a clear conclusion that no approach has yet succeeded in reversing the poor development of language in severely and profoundly deaf children; while Geers (1985) has argued that the most important ingredient in effective education of the deaf child is 'well structured educational programmes that are based on the realization that most deaf children require extremely careful, intensive, individualized instruction in order to realize their potential' (p.81).

Notes

1   For a detailed historical account of deaf education from Aristotle to the early part of the twentieth century, see Hodgson (1953).
2   For an overview of some of the debates see RNID (1976).
3   For a review of studies on various communication modes see Rodda and Grove (1987).
4   Of the sample of school children, 41 per cent had learned fingerspelling prior to the first testing. The children had come from a wide catchment area, and ten different primary schools were named where fingerspelling had been taught. Other places included Cub Scouts, the church, and home.

5 Integration into society

A profoundly deaf boy had an accident at school and was taken to the casualty department of a general hospital by a hearing teacher. The teacher went to make some enquiries, leaving the child sitting in the waiting area. She returned to find a nurse shouting at the deaf boy, who was very confused and unable to follow her distorted lip pattern. The teacher explained that she was with the child, so the nurse turned to the teacher and began shouting at her.

Although the above incident was related with some humour to the author, it serves to highlight some of the misconceptions that hearing people have about deaf people. It is a common misconception that if you shout loudly enough at a deaf person they will hear what you say. In reality the lip pattern becomes distorted and it becomes more difficult for the deaf person to lip read and understand what is being said.

Stokoe and Battison (1981, cited in Rodda and Grove 1987, p.89) have identified the frustration which arises for hearing people because of the inability to communicate effectively. They point out that the question 'What's the matter, are you deaf?' is an expression of frustration, accusation and anger, not an enquiry into the processing capacity of the person's ears. A person, whether deaf or hearing, who is not perceived as using or understanding language appropriately creates a tension that inhibits smooth social interaction. Higgins (1980) has shown that hearing people tend to be reluctant to repeat spoken messages, although deaf people frequently need the message repeated (often, rather than repeated, the message will be rephrased, confusing the deaf person even further).

Studies on bilingualism have shown that many misunderstandings arise between speakers of different languages (Appel and Muysken 1988). They argue that these interaction problems are expressions of inter-ethnic or inter-cultural differences, and they might become sources of inter-ethnic conflicts: 'People tend to judge each other often on the basis of their communicative behaviour . . . and . . . majority-language speakers negatively stereotype the non-native speakers, because "they do not know how to behave", "they are hardly civilized", etc.' (p.144). Higgins (1980) has argued that interaction between foreigners and natives resembles deaf–hearing encounters.

According to Rodda and Grove (1987), the frustration is compounded by the fact that deafness is an invisible handicap, therefore we expect deaf people to behave as if they hear, and are unprepared to cope with the realities of communicating and interacting with a person who does not hear. This can cause feelings of awkwardness or embarrassment on both sides. For example, during an interview with the author a profoundly deaf woman related:

> I hate going into the bank. When I say I'm deaf they shout. That distorts the lip pattern. When I changed my money to go on holiday to America the girl wouldn't explain anything to me because it took a long time to explain and people were queuing up behind.

Higgins (1980) suggested that reluctance to communicate by hearing people is often seen by the deaf as an indication that they are not fully accepted for what they are – people who may need a message repeated. He argued that, if hearing people's attitude changed towards the deaf so that messages were repeated, then the deaf might no longer be outsiders in a hearing world. Although Montgomery (1981b) made the point that, while acceptance of the deaf by hearing people is important, it can also attract the stigma of special provision so that the deaf are seen as handicapped, needing the assistance of hearing people. Alternatively, Higgins (1980) argued that a deaf person with good speech may be treated as hearing, and not get the required information.

According to Stokoe (1978), among the other factors enforcing the social isolation of the deaf from the hearing world is public opinion, as expressed in the attitudes of the hearing majority. There is an assumption that the deaf are inferior to hearing people, and the stereotype of the deaf as 'dumb'. He also claimed that 'there seems to be less public sympathy for the deaf apparently because of the ignorance of the gravity of the handicap and because of its invisibility' (p.24) (see also the findings of the present study regarding blindness and deafness, pages 69–70). 'Thus the deaf, first isolated from normal social relations by the fact of physical handicap, become segregated as a group through the operation of institutional patterns in the general culture' (Stokoe 1978, p.24). Higgins (1980) has also found that people who become deaf after speech has developed may stigmatize those who are born deaf.

Because of segregation by the hearing society, not surprisingly, over the years, deaf people have tended to congregate together and form themselves into groups. This has resulted in the development of a 'deaf community' and the notion of a 'deaf culture'.

The deaf community

'Community' can be defined as 'a body of people having common rights, interests, occupation, religion, nationality, etc.' (*Cassells Dictionary* 1970). According to Deuchar (1984), the defining characteristic of the deaf community seems to be its sign language. Higgins (1980) pointed out that membership in a deaf community is not associated with status. It must be achieved. It is achieved through:

- identification with the deaf world;
- shared experiences from being hearing-impaired;
- participation in the community's activities.

It appears that, in every country in which deaf people congregate together and form a sign language, a deaf community emerges. Woodward (1980), for instance, argued that the deaf French, like the deaf North Americans, have formed a community which is held together by self-identification as a deaf community member, language (French Sign Language), marital patterns and social organizations. The same is true in this country, with British Sign Language (BSL) as the defining characteristic.

Prior to the nineteenth century, the concept of a 'deaf community' did not exist. Deaf people were isolated and dispersed sporadically throughout the whole population, uneducated, undervalued and neglected by society. They were not seen as citizens with rights, but were at first despised, and later pitied, by an ignorant public.

During the nineteenth century attitudes of society towards the deaf gradually began to change, and so did the attitude of the deaf themselves. Campaigns for educating deaf children got under way, and at the same time a growing public sympathy spread throughout the UK so that religious and charitable movements began to administer welfare to the adult deaf. Initially this work was for the deaf, there was no suggestion of cooperation with the deaf, who were not regarded as equals (Hodgson 1953).

Welfare work began in the form of missions, where for the first time deaf adults were congregating together forming their own sign language and developing a growing corporate spirit. The first church for the deaf, St Saviour's in Oxford Street, London, was opened by Queen Victoria in 1873. By conferring royal patronage she brought into being the Royal Association in Aid of the Deaf and Dumb.

In 1836 the 'Charitable and Provident Society for Granting Pensions to the Aged Poor and Infirm Deaf and Dumb' had been founded as a recoil from the harshness of the Poor Law 1834. This society was reformed in 1890 as the British Deaf and Dumb Association, and became the British Deaf Association (BDA) in 1970. The society was founded in protest against the Royal Commission (HMSO 1889) which recommended oral education for deaf children following the 1880 Milan Conference (see page 65). Since that time the organization has taken up all aspects of deaf welfare, as well as consistently advocating the use of manual methods in deaf education (Deuchar 1984).

In 1911 the National Bureau for Promoting the General Welfare of the Deaf was founded, and reconstituted as the National Institute for the Deaf (NID) in 1923. On its fiftieth anniversary in 1961 it became the Royal National Institute for the Deaf (RNID), and acts as a resource centre for information relating to deafness (Ballantyne 1970).

Although the BDA produced a manual of sign language in 1960 (Goodridge 1960, cited in Deuchar 1984, p.41), it was not until the late 1970s, following an upsurge of interest by both linguists and psychologists into British Sign Language (BSL) and deaf education, that the association actually recognized BSL as a language in its own right. Research into BSL followed on from the work of Stokoe (1978) in the USA on his analysis of American Sign Language. Research units which were set up in Edinburgh and Bristol found that BSL was a true language, and of greater complexity than had ever been suspected (Ladd 1988). It seems that, with this realization, a new wave of confidence and optimism has spread through the deaf community, encouraging greater effort to improve the status of BSL.

During the 1970s the BDA established a communication skills programme supported by a grant from the Department of Health and Social Security. It aimed to promote publicity, study and teaching of sign language, and to set up a register of interpreters which would provide better training and professional status for sign language interpreters. As the programme came to an end in 1981, the Council for the Advancement of Communication with Deaf People (CACDP) was set up, to pursue similar aims (Deuchar 1984).

BDA interpreters were first used in 1981 for political conferences, including the Labour Party Conference, where some of the party leader's speech was shown on television in sign language at peak viewing time, thus introducing many hearing people to BSL for the first time (Deuchar 1984).

Two further pressure groups also emerged during this period: the National Union of the Deaf (NUD) was set up in 1976 entirely through the initiative of deaf people, to promote the interests of the deaf, and the Deaf Broadcasting Campaign (DBC), developed during the late 1970s with the aim of promoting the use of subtitling and sign language on television (Deuchar 1984).

A pilot programme was broadcast in 1979 on BBC television entitled 'Signs of Life'. Following this the magazine programme *See Hear* was established in 1981, then programmes on ITV and Channel 4 (Ladd 1988). A television course for teaching BSL to beginners was developed and first broadcast in 1988 (Miles 1988).

In June 1988 the European Parliament gave unanimous support to a resolution to recognize the sign languages of member states (EEC 1988). Mrs Eileen Lemass, MEP Chairman of the Youth, Culture, Education and Sport Committee of the European Parliament, put the case for official recognition. She argued that if sign language was officially recognized it could lead to equal opportunities in education, employment, the provision of interpreters in a variety of settings, more television programmes in sign language and greater access to the political scene through the provision of sign language interpreters at party political conferences and television coverage. She stated:

> There are over 500 000 profoundly deaf people in the EEC. By officially recognising the national Sign Languages of each country, the European community will open the doors of opportunity to Deaf people . . . it will offer Deaf people the same opportunities and the same access to information that hearing people have long taken for granted. (EEC 1988)

This decision, seen as a victory for the deaf community, was an important landmark after many years of struggling and campaigning for recognition that hearing-impaired people are equal to hearing people and not second-class citizens.

Many of the arguments regarding the integration of the deaf into society are similar to those concerning mainstreaming in education (see Chapter 4). A strong school of thought exists that integration of the deaf into hearing society must be achieved at all costs. For example, at a British audiological conference, talking about deaf children being educated orally, Clark (1983) claimed that the ability to use to the full whatever residual hearing they have has allowed deaf children to develop a conventional communicative competence which gives them confidence to take their full place in normal hearing society. Yet Deuchar (1984) has argued that the deaf constitute an ethnic minority who do not want to be assimilated into wider society, but want to retain their own culture. There are many accounts by both deaf and hearing people demonstrating the difficulties deaf people face in hearing society (for example, Ladd 1981; Hay 1981; Rees 1983; Marchant 1987; Jones 1986). From some of these accounts it can be seen that deaf people are often considered to be intellectually impaired on first encounter with a hearing person because of poor speech intelligibility. Difficulties with communication can lead to frustration and confusion, and eventual isolation and loneliness. Membership of the deaf community offers deaf people not only the chance to express themselves and share experiences, but also a sense of self-identity and belonging as a community member (Woodward 1980).

Farb (1977) has pointed out that language has a function of displaying an in-group solidarity, and maintaining a boundary against outsiders. Just as language is used by doctors and lawyers for this purpose, BSL performs the same function for the deaf community.

Communication and British Sign Language

Communication is central to the debate about integration of the deaf into hearing society. Problems with communication affect the whole socialization process for a deaf child, and have far-reaching implications for the future in social, emotional and economic terms. Communication involves far more than just imparting information. Gregory (1976) argued that it is a way of maintaining contact, enhancing relationships and bringing people closer.

With his concept of 'phatic communion', Malinowski (1927) showed that, even in what to an observer might seem to be apparently meaningless conversation, there is an element of social cohesiveness. A mutual understanding exists which draws people together within a secure framework of social rules and norms of behaviour. With this shared understanding it is possible for someone who does not speak a language fluently to get by in a social situation. (Anecdotal evidence of such instances has been conveyed to the author by Mackinnon and Allen.)

But without a shared understanding communication is not possible. For example, I remember my first encounter with a profoundly deaf 3-year-old boy, while visiting a school for the deaf where Total Communication was used. School had just finished for the day and the class teacher was occupied elsewhere. The boy came up to me and signed something that I did not understand. I knew that he had asked a question, but I had no understanding of what he was saying. He was trying so hard to communicate, but I was unable to respond. I couldn't answer 'yes' or 'no' because I didn't know what he had asked, and a wrong answer might have led to further confusion and misunderstanding. His expression conveyed to me a sense of hurt and puzzlement. (Some time later I discovered that he had asked me if I was going home.)

Furth (1978) argued that the society into which children are born and grow up is as much a continuous and living part of themselves as any other part of their psychology. The child develops an understanding of society by exploring and testing out personal encounters. If hearing people continually fail to respond to deaf children when they initiate conversation this is likely to have some effect over their self-esteem and self-image – how much effect is an area still to be explored.

Drawing parallels between the status of BSL and West Indian Creole, Ladd and Edwards (1982) have argued that there is a long tradition of negative attitudes towards non-standard varieties of language in the UK, which have only recently begun to be explained in terms of social and historical development rather than as the result of laziness or stupidity, and that often these negative attitudes can be found among members of the deaf community itself. They argue that such negative attitudes towards BSL can have a profound effect on the self-concept of deaf people.

Research for the present study suggests that the general public tend to view sign language positively. A significant difference was found between teachers of the deaf and the other groups tested with the statement 'Sign Language helps deaf people to mix with hearing people.' Only 29 per cent of teachers of the deaf agreed with the statement. However, a majority in all the other groups tested agreed, that is, 70 per cent of the general public; and of the school children, 83 per cent of the Signing Experience (SE) group, closely followed by 77 per cent of the Partial Hearing Control (PHC) group, and 68 per cent of the Signing Control (SC) group. The Partial Hearing Experience (PHE) group had the lowest agreement response of 54 per cent (see Figure 5.1)

This statement can be viewed from two different perspectives. Sign language can only help deaf people to mix with hearing people providing there is a shared understanding of its meaning. Thus it can be seen by some as an isolating factor, keeping the deaf away from hearing society, as a separate group with their own language, or alternatively it can be seen as the means of a mutual form of communication between two different groups of people (as happened in places such as Martha's Vineyard – see page 118). It would seem that the teachers of the deaf were mainly viewing sign language from the former perspective, while the other groups were viewing it from the latter.

In order for sign language to help deaf people to mix with hearing people, hearing people must be prepared to at least acquire some basic knowledge of it. Sign language can be used as a bridge to the hearing for deaf people if it is learned by those closest to deaf people in their daily lives (Ladd and Edwards 1982). Brennan (1989) endorsed this by pointing out that research has shown that, however 'bad' a hearing person's signing is, deaf children are able to transpose it in their very capable brains into quite acceptable BSL.

A study by Kyle and Allsop (1982) in which young deaf people (aged 16–25) were interviewed about communication methods suggested that not only do young deaf adults wish to use sign language in learning situations, but also that they recognize the importance of speech and lip reading. They claimed that the argument that if deaf people use sign they will not be able to communicate with hearing people who do not use sign has been used as

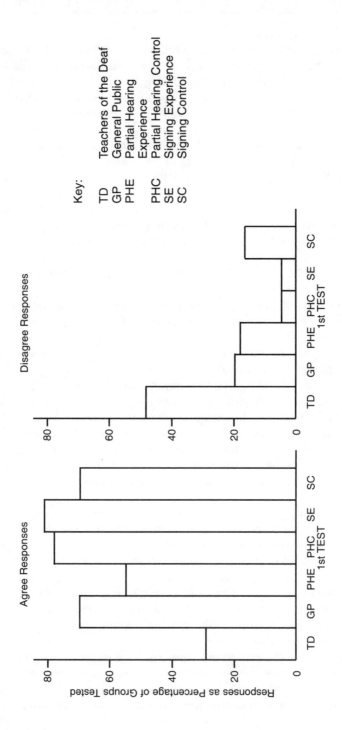

Figure 5.1 Agree/disagree responses to the statement: 'Sign language helps deaf people to mix with hearing people'

a justification for not teaching signing in schools. They also claimed that the penalty for not allowing sign language at school is that deaf children do not learn to communicate with other deaf people. Kyle and Allsop pointed out that there is nothing to suggest that sign language is any more difficult to learn for hearing people than any other second language.

The power of language

According to Schlesinger (1985), power is a theoretical construct related to the sense of having the competence, ability and opportunity to influence and shape the environment, and powerlessness is the absence of this quality.[1]

It has been argued that language provides the most powerful hold that society has over individuals. It is the first institution encountered, and all other institutions build themselves on language (Berger and Berger 1978).

Speech is a very powerful tool, strongly linked to position in society and to social mobility. Bernstein (1971, 1973) studied the way in which speech enters into power relationships of society, and argued that different kinds of language codes reflect modes of social integration.

People are judged intellectually on the basis of minor differences in pronunciation. As soon as a person speaks, conclusions are drawn by the listener about social class background, level of education, sex, ethnicity, geographical origin, etc. and, rightly or wrongly, expectations are built up on the basis of these speech cues (Stubbs 1979; Trudgill 1981; Edwards 1987).

It has also been suggested by Scherer (1979) that, in some contexts, vocal qualities are more crucial for forming impressions about the speaker than either what is said or visual clues. If this is so, then a deaf person with poor speech is immediately socially disadvantaged in the hearing culture. All evidence points to well-adjusted children evaluating themselves positively (Thompson 1974), and it is well recognized that the self-esteem of the child in school is a crucial factor in his or her learning at all levels of success (Hart 1985; Shavelson and Bolus 1982; Marsh et al 1983); yet it appears that deaf children are exposed to an education system which reinforces a sense of failure and low level of self-esteem.

Davis (1976) has argued that society unwittingly reduces the deaf to second-class citizens by implying that they are not capable of doing what hearing people do, and suggested that parents and teachers over-protect deaf children. In turn over-protection can lead to low self-expectation and under-achievement. An examination of the deaf in society confirms their low status, because relatively few are professional workers or hold high administrative positions. (This is also true in the USA – for example, Schein and Delk 1974; Jarvik et al 1969). This view is endorsed by Ladd and Edwards (1982), who discovered that figures relating to the employment of the deaf in the UK do not exist. From all the informed estimates, the absolute maximum of deaf workers in white-collar jobs would appear to be 10 per cent (compared with 8 per cent for black people and 40 per cent for the rest of the population), and 'both the Deaf and the West Indians constitute groups with extremely low status in British society' (p.106).

Because Standard English has more status and prestige than any other English dialect, the evaluation of dialects and accents have important implications for minority groups. Trudgill (1981) has argued that 'The scientific study of language has convinced most scholars that all languages, and correspondingly all dialects, are equally "good" as linguistic systems' (p.20); therefore judgements concerning the correctness and purity of linguistic varieties are social rather than linguistic. Any apparent inferiority is due only to their association with speakers from underprivileged, low-status groups.

As attitudes towards a language reflect attitudes towards the person using that language (Bellugi 1976), if sign language is denigrated or considered to be inferior to spoken English, then deaf children will feel denigrated and their self-esteem will be reduced.

There was a general consensus in the present study, among all the groups tested, that sign language is a proper language. Figure 5.2 shows the 'disagree' responses to the statement 'Although sign language may be useful, it isn't really a proper language.' Teachers of the deaf had the highest 'disagree' response rate (82 per cent) and the children with the partial-hearing unit in the school the lowest (PHE and PHC both 42 per cent).

Some interesting differences were found with the statement 'If a person is born deaf and is taught sign language as a baby, English is their second language.' Of the teachers of the deaf, 64 per cent agreed with this statement compared with 30 per cent of the general public. Only 4 per cent of teachers of the deaf disagreed, compared with 24 per cent of the general public (see Figure 5.3).

At the first testing the sample of school children tended to be in agreement with the statement (although a large number in each category were non-committal in their responses, answering either in the 'don't know' or 'neutral' categories). Of the children in the PHE and SE groups, 50 per cent agreed with the statement compared with 46 per cent (PHC) and 36 per cent (SC).

At the second testing, at the end of the school year, this had altered. The PHE and SC groups remained fairly constant (48 per cent and 39 per cent respectively) while the PHC group had dropped to 33 per cent. The biggest difference was found in the SE group, where the agreement response rate dropped from 50 per cent to 27 per cent, and the disagreement response rose from 13 per cent to 36 per cent (see Figure 5.4). This result could reflect the difficulties associated with learning a new language, as many of the children

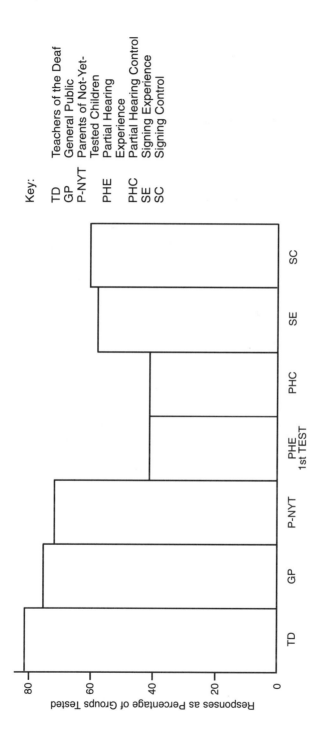

Key:

TD   Teachers of the Deaf
GP   General Public
P-NYT   Parents of Not-Yet-
        Tested Children
PHE   Partial Hearing
        Experience
PHC   Partial Hearing Control
SE   Signing Experience
SC   Signing Control

Figure 5.2   Disagree responses to the statement: 'Although sign language may be useful, it isn't really a proper language'

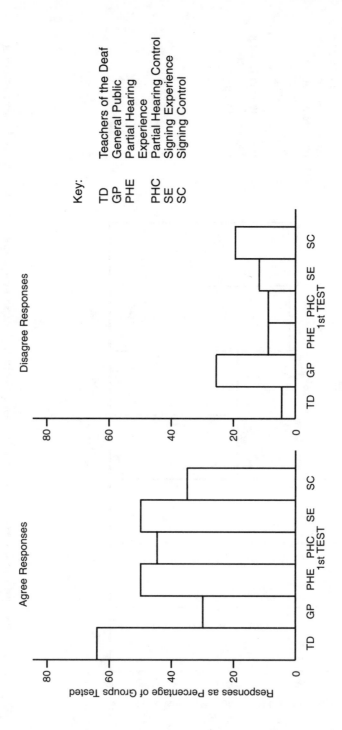

Figure 5.3 Agree/disagree responses to the statement: 'If a person is born deaf and is taught sign language as a baby, English is their second language'

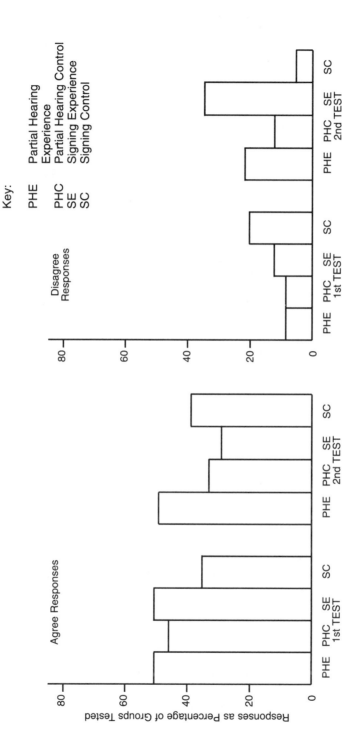

Figure 5.4 Comparison of school children's agree/disagree responses (1st and 2nd tests) to the statement: 'If a person is born deaf and is taught sign language as a baby, English is their second language'

tested in this group were learning sign in order to communicate with their profoundly deaf peers. Without fluency in sign language they may have found it difficult to comprehend that this could be the main form of communication in a home (as has happened with some hearing professionals, who claim that signing is only a form of gesture and not a proper language: for example, Dale 1972; DES 1968). However, the reason for the change in attitude is more likely to be because the children were learning Signed English, not BSL (that is, they were learning signs based on BSL but in English word order), and so were likely to perceive sign language to be another form of English.

So, although a high consensus was found concerning sign as a proper language, there was less agreement that it could also be considered as a first language, with English as the second.

Schlesinger (1978) has argued that the growth of self-acceptance is accompanied by early awareness of human differences, which ideally can be accepted either joyfully or neutrally. Yet she has noted that many normal-hearing parents of deaf youngsters find it very difficult to accept that their children are different from hearing children, and attempt to force them to behave as hearing children do. Some parents even refuse to let their children wear hearing aids, and inhibit the use of both gestures and voice, so that their children learn from early on that their 'deficiencies' (her word), such as hearing aids, vocal quality and use of gesture, are devalued by overall society.

Some differences were found among the various groups tested for this study on the statement 'As a society we push out deaf people' (see Figure 5.5). Approximately half the samples of both teachers of the deaf and the general public were in agreement with the statement (50 per cent and 51 per cent respectively). Only 4 per cent of teachers of the deaf disagreed with the statement, compared with 32 per cent of the general public (30 per cent of teachers of the deaf and 17 per cent of the general public gave a non-committal response). So, in general, both of these adult groups tended to agree that the deaf are pushed out by society.

In contrast to this, the majority of the school children in all the groups tested disagreed with the statement (see Figure 5.5). The lowest 'agree' response came from the PHE group (4 per cent), followed by the SE group (18 per cent), then both control groups (28 per cent).

Building on the work of Piaget, Selman (1976, cited in Rubin 1980) has described a stepladder progression in children's friendship awareness, where by the age of 11–12 years the child comes to view close friendship as a relationship that takes shape over a period of time. According to this view, children work out for themselves what social relationships are all about on the basis of their actual encounters with others. Through their interactions with peers, children discover that other children are similar to them in some

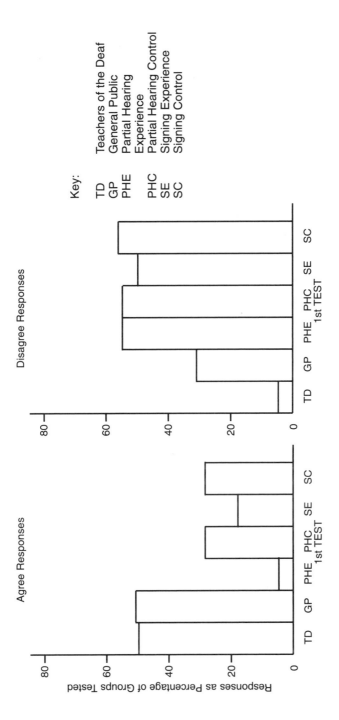

Figure 5.5   Agree/disagree responses to the statement: 'As a society we push out deaf people'

respects and different in others. At this stage (11–12 years), friends are seen as providers of intimacy and support. Close friends need to be able to share interests and have mutually agreeable personalities; for example, in his own study, Rubin (1980) describes the response of a 13-year-old boy when asked why a particular boy was his friend. He responded: 'We like the same kind of things. We speak the same language' (p.39).

Clearly, at this age ease of communication is a very important factor in both the development and maintenance of friendships. For the present study some significant differences were found on the statement 'When I am with a deaf person I find it hard to talk to them.'

It was expected that teachers of the deaf would find it easier to talk to deaf people because of their experience, and this was found to be the case. Only 11 per cent of the teachers of the deaf agreed with the statement, compared with a much higher agreement rate from all the other groups tested, which ranged from 34 per cent (general public) to 63 per cent (PHC group) (see Figure 5.6).

Among the school children, at the first testing the main differences were found between the PHE and PHC groups, with 63 per cent of the PHC group agreeing with the statement compared with 35 per cent of the PHE group. Both the SE and SC groups gave a similar response, tending to agree with the statement (50 per cent and 56 per cent respectively). However, a significant difference was found between the two experience groups at the second testing. The agreement rate dropped and the disagreement rate rose in all groups except the SE group, where the reverse occurred (see Figure 5.7).

These responses highlight differences in experience between the two groups. The child in the partial-hearing unit had very good speech development and lip reading skills, whereas the profoundly deaf pupils had poor speech articulation and relied heavily on signing for their communication.

If, as already suggested, ease of communication is an important factor in the development of friendships, then deaf children have a major hurdle to overcome in this particular situation with their hearing peers, who are only just beginning to learn to sign. The hearing children are already in a majority-language situation. Discussing normal-hearing bilingual children, Arnberg (1987) argued that, because of the adjustments that a bilingual child has to make to the majority language and culture, it can be a very difficult situation for a child to be placed directly into a majority-language class. The same can be applied to deaf children.

According to Webster and Wood (1989), integration is a process and not a target to aim for, and ultimately it is the quality of a child's experience which is most important. They point out that integration should be judged on the amount of real sharing of experiences which takes place, particularly within the classroom, and that: 'In its fullest sense, integration is functional and

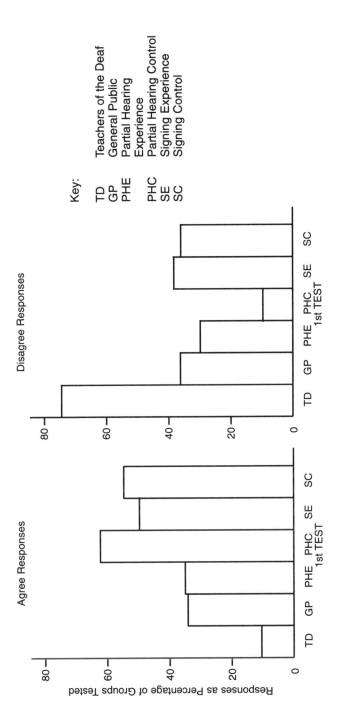

Figure 5.6 Agree/disagree responses to the statement: 'When I am with a deaf person I find it hard to talk to them'

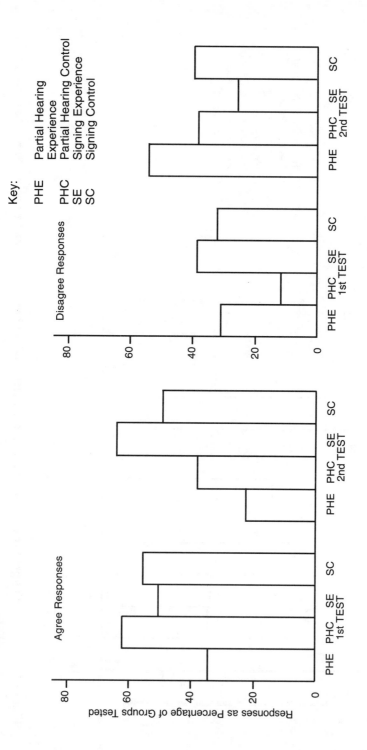

Figure 5.7 Comparison of school children's agree/disagree responses (1st and 2nd tests) to the statement: 'When I am with a deaf person I find it hard to talk to them'

implies that children participate in a wholly meaningful way in the learning community of the school' (p.26).

The experience of any children, both in the classroom and in wider society, will be affected by the attitudes of others towards them. Frequently encounters between hearing and deaf people result in feelings of awkwardness or embarrassment. For example, a restaurant owner interviewed for the present study described her feelings when encountering her first profoundly deaf customers:

> We have four profoundly deaf customers who come in regularly for a meal . . . When they first came in it felt a bit strange. I felt uncomfortable. I didn't really know how to react. I've never ever met a deaf person before – not on that level – initially I felt embarrassment. I find it difficult to communicate quite often with hearing people. With deaf people you've suddenly got an added barrier. We get on great now.

In another interview the father of a profoundly deaf boy explained:

> I think it's an uphill battle getting people to try to understand or get involved with deaf people because its just a non-interest . . . There are disfigurement problems with loads of people . . . If people are honest – any handicap; [for example] Deaf; people . . . go to all sorts of ends to get out of trying to talk to deaf people. They feel embarrassed. Same with a handicapped person. Once you know deaf people it's different – it's getting over – people dive out of the way and stuff.

For the present study, the statement 'When I am with a deaf person I sometimes feel awkward' was included in the questionnaire.

On the first testing, significant differences were found between teachers of the deaf, and the general public, PHC and SE groups (see Figure 5.8).

Significant differences were also found between the first and second testing for the school children. At the first testing, 24 per cent of the PHE and SC groups agreed with the statement, compared with 68 per cent of the PHC and 46 per cent of the SE groups. By the end of the school year, in every group the 'agree' responses had fallen and the 'disagree' responses had risen (see Figure 5.9). In the SE group, there was a 25 per cent increase in children who disagreed with the statement (from 25 per cent to 50 per cent). The lowest 'agree' responses were found in the PHE group (13 per cent) and SC group (14 per cent).

So, although by the end of the school year the children in the SE group found it hard to talk to their profoundly deaf peers, at the same time they felt less awkward with them. Rubin (1980) has suggested that the development of communication skills through interaction with one's peers may itself be an important prerequisite for the acquisition of skills specifically related to friendship. It would seem from these results that frequent contact between deaf and hearing children reduces the sense of awkwardness on the part of

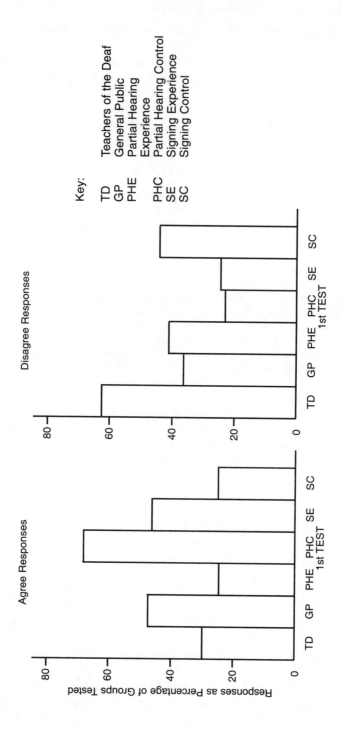

Figure 5.8 Agree/disagree responses to the statement: 'When I am with a deaf person I sometimes feel awkward'

hearing children. (Further investigations would need to be made to find out if the same is true of deaf children.)

According to Schlesinger (1986), research based on findings with immigrant minority children is being applied to deaf children. She considered that deaf children are like minority children in that there is a deaf culture and a deaf language different from the majority culture and language. However, they are also different from other minority children in that they do not necessarily share that minority status with their hearing parents. This is true in 90–95 per cent of cases in the USA (Schein and Delk 1974), and 90 per cent of cases in the UK (Denmark 1990; Llewellyn-Jones 1987; Conrad 1981).

Deaf children, like immigrant children, may move away from the culture of their parents to a new culture, but whereas most immigrants move from a minority to a majority status, the deaf may move from a majority to a minority status (Schlesinger 1986).

According to Trudgill (1981), it is the attitudes of society as a whole towards language that need to be changed in order for ethnic minority groups to be accepted in society. The same argument can be applied to the deaf as a minority group. Sprott (1958) pointed out that a fundamental notion of a social group is the consciousness of belonging – there is a group because 'we' think 'we' belong to it. Pressures are exerted on hearing children by their peers to conform to linguistic norms (Haugen 1962), and it is from a sense of social cohesiveness and feelings of identity formed by the common language bond that a sense of power develops (Pride 1974). It can be seen that this similar process is happening within the deaf community, particularly since the recent work on BSL has established it as a language in its own right.

In the case of deaf people, bilingualism involves a positive attitude towards both the deaf and towards sign language, but this is possibly threatening for hearing people because it could alter the balance of status and control. When discussing power in social relationships, Mennell (1974) argued that it must be considered in terms of probability, as it is always relative and never absolute. He claimed that social relationships are never static, so neither is power. It is always shifting and changing, and needs to be seen as a process. Endorsing this view, Schlesinger (1985) argued that the sense of power is culturally determined and context-bound, and therefore is potentially changeable. While deaf people feel denigrated and are treated as second-class citizens, they will also feel a sense of powerlessness which can also, directly or indirectly, affect the capacity to learn.

According to Mennell, in order to exercise power it is necessary to have some control over what the other decides. In the case of BSL it has been the all-powerful educators in both teaching and training institutions who have exercised control over which language the deaf will use, even though, since

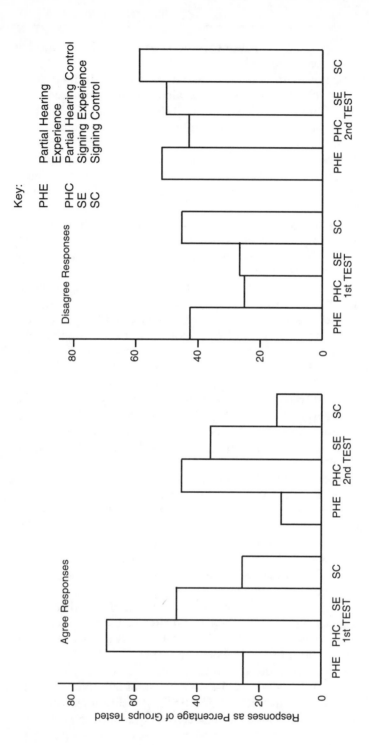

Figure 5.9 Comparison of school children's agree/disagree responses (1st and 2nd tests) to the statement: 'When I am with a deaf person I sometimes feel awkward'

the end of the nineteenth century, the deaf themselves have been protesting against the methods being used in their education.

Although educators may believe that they are working in the best interests of deaf children, it would seem that the issues involved are strongly linked to power and control, with the dominant majority battling to remain in control over a minority group who, instead of giving in and 'doing what they're told', have instead become more determined to fight for what they believe to be right. The fact that the battle is still raging a century after the deaf began to join in in force gives some indication of how strongly the majority are trying to maintain their position of power.

The attitudes of professionals who hold key positions in training institutions are of vital importance because of their potential to influence others – for example, in the establishments which train people to become teachers of the deaf. Prior to their training, because the incidence of severe and profound deafness is relatively low, it is likely that many of the people who decide to teach deaf children will have very little experience with deafness or the educational methods used with this group. On entering a training institution they will be taught the 'correct' way to work with deaf children. It is very hard to question any method without experience, particularly if everyone else around believes in that method. Practices, beliefs and attitudes get passed on from generation to generation of students, frequently without question. (The same can be true in any institution, for example, in nursing, which Menzies (1960) described as an occupation probably more resistant to change than most.)

Until very recently, deaf students were not accepted at teacher training establishments. After the Milan Conference of 1880, educational policy in the UK involved the removal of deaf teachers, who were seen as a subversive influence on deaf children in that they continued to use BSL. By the First World War virtually all had been removed from their posts (Ladd 1988).

In attempting to fight for their rights the deaf pose another threat to society. By definition deaf people are 'disabled' people with 'special needs'. Since the nineteenth century the public has been increasingly sympathetic in its attitude towards people with disabilities. Yet, in order to maintain that sympathy, people categorized into such groups are expected to act as if they are disabled (Goffman 1973).

By forming pressure groups and demanding changes in education, the deaf are posing threats to established institutions. Conrad (1981) argued that we are discussing a social and cultural revolution leading towards a society where deaf people are encouraged to use sign language instead of being punished for it.

Cultural and political influences

It has been argued by Ingleby (1974) that 'practically every act in relation to a child, from birth and even before, reflects constraints dictated by that child's place in the political system' (p.297), and 'the political system is inextricably present in the most basic aspects of child rearing' (p.298). Children's mentality, their formation of ideas about their own needs, and the responses that can be expected from the world around them, boil down to expectations from early experience, and the influence of their environment cannot be disentangled from the socio-economic determinants of that environment. Ingleby suggested that the way people exercise power and control in relationships, and how people are trained to act and think, have to be understood in terms of their position in the political order.

Socio-economic effects have a bearing on child development, and 'cultures of failure' can result from persistent poverty (Bruner 1970, 1974). According to Schlesinger (1985), large-scale research has shown that certain characteristics are common both to many deaf people and to many poor individuals – these include academic retardation, impulsiveness, attention to the here and now rather than to the future, and restricted vocational achievement. For Schlesinger, the common factor underlying what she has termed the 'maladaptive patterns' frequently associated with both deafness and poverty is a sense of powerlessness.

An early study of attitudes towards school (Hess and Shipman 1965) showed that middle-class parents socialize their children to go to school, whereas working-class mothers tell their children to be obedient and stay out of trouble. Cazden (1972, cited in Schlesinger 1985) claimed that deaf children resemble disadvantaged children in their attitudes towards school. In a comparison of hearing and deaf children aged 8 years, 89 per cent of hearing children said they went to school 'to learn' but only 39 per cent of deaf children gave that response. The remainder went because they 'had to'.

Schlesinger considered that a sense of powerlessness is developed mainly in the toddler years through parental and caregiver attitudes; when children and parents are able to communicate reciprocally and successfully, they feel more powerful, the interchanges between parent and child are marked by a greater sense of mastery and less need for control, and parents are able to foster and encourage autonomy and the motivation to learn in their children.

Normal-hearing parents of a deaf child belong to a minority group without the benefit of support systems that a minority culture often provides. This point was discussed at a conference in 1989, when the hearing father of a profoundly deaf 9-year-old boy raised the question 'Where is the deaf culture for deaf children of hearing parents?' He pointed out that his family were Roman Catholic, yet there were no deaf Catholic priests available to his son; that his son had attended a summer camp run by the

BDA, yet there were no deaf adults present – it was run by hearing people, and that, although he and his wife had learned BSL and attended their local deaf club, there were no deaf children who attended. He asked 'Where is the deaf culture?'

At the same conference, Brennan (1989) called for greater cooperation between both the deaf and hearing communities, and suggested that perhaps the deaf could also do more to encourage hearing parents with deaf children to integrate those children into the deaf community. She pointed out that it is not very helpful waiting until these children reach the age of 16 years and then complaining that they cannot sign. She realized that many deaf people argue that they want their deaf clubs to themselves; they do not want to spend their leisure time with hearing people, but want to feel that they can relax and communicate freely and easily with others. Yet she questioned how hearing parents can learn BSL without the help of the deaf community, and argued that deaf children are the responsibility of everyone.

Notes

1   For a detailed discussion on the development of ideas regarding the power of language the reader is referred to Brown and Gilman (1960), Fishman (1972, 1975) and Illich (1981).

6 Stigma, self-esteem and self-image

Introduction

In this chapter the relationship between self-esteem and the stigma associated with deafness is explored. The concepts of self-esteem (as defined by Coopersmith 1967) and stigma (specifically related to Goffman 1973) are discussed, with particular emphasis on the communication difficulties experienced between deaf and hearing people.

Drawing on examples from data collected for the present study, consideration is then given to the possible ways in which hearing-impaired people may react to their potentially stigmatizing condition. A typology in the form of a two-by-two table has been developed by the author as an aid to understanding possible reactions.

This is followed by further discussion about self-esteem, and the importance of parents and the peer group in the growth of self-esteem is highlighted.

Stigma and self-esteem

The word 'stigma' originated from the Greeks, who used it to refer to bodily signs which were supposed to expose something unusual and bad about the moral status of a person. Today the term is widely used, but tends to be applied more to 'disgrace' surrounding a person than to actual bodily evidence.

'Self-esteem' refers to

the evaluation which the individual makes and customarily maintains with regard to himself; it expresses an attitude of approval or disapproval, and indicates the extent to which the individual believes himself to be capable, significant, successful, and worthy. In short, self-esteem is a personal judgement of worthiness that is expressed in the attitudes the individual holds towards himself. It is a subjective experience which the individual conveys to others by verbal reports and other overt expressive behaviours. (Coopersmith 1967, pp.4–5)

As was discussed in Chapters 2 and 3, people view the world through their own perspective and create their own reality from the information they receive and transmit. Communication is the essence of human relationships. Without a shared understanding, confusion, frustration and isolation may result. Misunderstandings can occur between people for a multitude of reasons. Confidence and self-esteem play a major part in interactions, and can affect a person's whole way of communicating, including posture, expression of thoughts and feelings, tone of voice, etc.

For example, when someone is feeling negative or depressed they tend to receive a negative response, and this can be a reinforcing phenomenon. Mood can affect the way people perceive and are perceived. An innocent comment or joke may be taken lightheartedly on one occasion, or experienced as a hurtful insult on another, depending on the mood of the people interacting at the time. Equally, an intentionally hurtful or sarcastic comment may be found to be amusing, or may be brushed off, ignored or 'taken to heart', depending on mood. We choose how we interpret and react to the intentions of others.

Even in everyday communication, signals can easily be misread because of differences in the use of words, accents, ways of expressing the self, etc. The chances of cross-cultural misunderstandings occurring are far greater when all the factors which go to make up communication are considered (speech, facial expression, body posture and gesture, eye contact, proximity, physical orientation, etc.). Birdwhistell (1970) contended that no gesture or body motion has been found which has the same social meaning in all societies, while Hall (1979) argued that all interactions require interpretation according to the culture of those who are interacting.

For people who are deaf, the chances of misunderstandings occurring during everyday interactions are far greater than for normal-hearing people. When people interact they expect the other to conform to particular forms of behaviour (Berger 1979), and they use information obtained in the initial interaction to make predictions about future behaviour (Berger 1975). Conversations between the deaf and normal-hearing can be fraught with difficulty. Higgins (1980) argued that the assumptions and practices of those who hear have a profound impact on the lives of those who do not hear. He found that hearing people are reluctant to repeat spoken messages to deaf people, even though deaf people often do not understand a spoken message the first time. Higgins cites Furfey and Harte (1964), who demonstrated that encounters between the deaf and hearing are often strained, awkward and confusing, and that increased contact between the deaf and hearing does not necessarily increase communication or understanding; and Emerton and Rothman (1978) have shown that hearing people may have less, rather than more, positive attitudes towards deaf people after interacting with them (p.143). It has been argued by Goffman (1973) that society establishes a means of categorizing people and decides on what is normal for each person in these categories – that is, we make assumptions about people and how we expect them to be, and if someone doesn't fit in with these expectations they are reduced to a 'not-so-good-as-us' level and are stigmatized accordingly.

Similarly, society uses stereotyping as another means of categorization. A stereotype refers to oversimplified, fixed and usually fallacious conceptions which people hold about other people (Lindesmith et al 1975). Once they have been formed, stereotypes tend to persist even in the face of contradictory evidence and experience. Gergen and Gergen (1981) suggested that stereotypes influence many daily actions and can distort reality. This can lead to important errors about people, which can maintain biased behaviour and negative attitudes towards certain groups who are 'not like us', and can create major social problems.

As was found in the study by Vandell et al (1982), hearing-impaired preschool children were perceived as different from their hearing peers, and the hearing children persistently refused to interact with them. Also, Graham (1986) argued that hearing children are likely to ignore a child who cannot respond readily to requests. As peers constitute one of the groups that make up 'significant others' in a child's life (see Chapter 2), a strong possiblity exists that hearing-impaired children will begin to perceive themselves as 'different' from an early age, and run the risk of becoming stigmatized.

Goffman (1973) suggested that two processes are occurring at the same time. The stigmatized individual defines himself as no different from any other human being, while at the same time both he and other people around him define him as someone different. Through socialization he learns and incorporates the standpoint of the normal person, so he acquires the identity and beliefs of wider society, and the general idea of what it would be like to possess a stigma, while in another phase he learns that he possesses the stigma and the consequences of having it. Stigma involves a two-role social process in which every individual participates in both roles at some point in life. Goffman considers that the normal and the stigmatized are not persons, but rather perspectives.

In her personal account of deafness, Jessica Rees (1983) argued that a deaf person with a self-perception radically different from the way others see them is likely to be maladjusted. Ridicule and misunderstanding occurred when she was at school with hearing children because she was unable to follow what was going on. Her self-confidence deteriorated and she became withdrawn and showed signs of stress. She emphasizes the importance of the perceptions of the peer group in accepting a deaf person. For example, when she discovered that children in her class envied her for wearing ear phones, she changed from feeling embarrassed and conspicuous to enjoying wearing them.

From his *dramaturgical interpretations of social interaction*, Goffman (1976, Ch.6) argued that every movement and action can be used to create impressions, and that, in shaping these impressions, the individual is also influencing the way in which others will respond to him or her. Coopersmith (1967) defines the ability to influence and control others as 'power' (p.38), and argued that success in the area of power is measured by the person's ability to influence the course of action by controlling their own behaviour and that of other individuals, and that 'In any given situation such power is revealed by the recognition and respect the individual receives from others and by the weight that is given to his opinions and rights' (p.40). Goffman claimed that all behaviour can serve the function of controlling others, while Higgins (1980) argued that the world is both created and controlled by those who hear, particularly in the areas of education and employment.

It has been suggested by Gergen and Gergen (1981) that, for people who have problems with managing relationships effectively, one reason could be an inability to read the cues given out by other people. This is certainly a problem in many encounters between deaf and hearing people, and was highlighted by Meyerson (1948) in his study on the dynamics of disability, in which he created experimental deafness in a number of children and adults by plugging their ears with a cotton and wax preparation for 24 hours. The reduction in acuity, as measured by a pure-tone audiometer, was approximately 30 dB in the speech range, which is a relatively slight handicap (see Chapter 9).

It was recognized that this was not a 'natural' situation. The subjects knew that it was an experiment, and also knew that the plugs would be removed in 24 hours, or sooner if wished. Nevertheless, Meyerson found that it was possible to observe practically all of the behavioural phenomena that have been ascribed to hard-of-hearing persons. Introspections of college students included withdrawal from social situations, aggression and irritability, suspiciousness, bluffing, inappropriate behaviour, misunderstanding and restlessness.

Observation of the behaviour of primary school children who wore plugs for a day at school revealed that there was definite avoidance or less active seeking of social contacts, increase in tension or restlessness, delayed reaction or non-reaction to verbal clues, greater alertness to non-verbal clues, increase in 'bored', 'stupid' or 'inappropriate' behaviour, increase in evidence of fatigue and irritability, changes in quality and intensity of voice, and attempts at concealment of the hearing loss by 'preoccupations'.

Meyerson concluded (as did Goffman later throughout his works) that 'The socially and psychologically undesirable behaviour that has been reported for physically handicapped persons does not arise because the disabled are different kinds of people, but because they have been subjected to different kinds of life experiences' (Meyerson 1948, p.71).

Berger and Bradac (1982) argued that language is used to exert control in relationships, and may also be a way of reducing our uncertainties, both about the other person and ourselves; and Scherer (1979) suggested that, in some contexts, vocal qualities are more critical for forming impressions about the speaker than either the actual content of what is said or visual clues. If this is true for hearing people, then how much more serious are the implications for profoundly deaf people, many of whom have difficulty in pronouncing words.

Studies, such as the one by Meyerson, and Goffman's work on stigma, have serious implications for deaf people. There is nothing outwardly unusual or odd about a deaf person until they attempt to communicate with a hearing person, when areas of complication are set up. Often assumptions are made about a person from initial interaction. Deaf people may be wrongly assumed to be mentally handicapped or even drunk.

The following example, related to the author by the mother of a profoundly deaf man, Derek, in his mid-30s, illustrates this point. Derek had a car and had been out driving and had, it seems, been in collision with another car. The mother explained:

> The phone rang at 11.45 pm. It was the police. 'We've got your son here. There's been an accident. There's some question of him having been drinking.'

As a child, Derek had been misdiagnosed as mentally retarded instead of deaf, and had been educated in a school for the educationally subnormal. He had learned neither spoken English nor sign language, and was unable to make himself understood. Two subsequent blood tests clearly showed that his blood alcohol level was well below the legal limit. The driver of the other car (who, from information gathered after the event, appeared to have been speeding) latched on to the idea that Derek was drunk, because of his poor speech articulation, as a means of clearing himself. The police initially took this at face value and prosecuted Derek. Fortunately, after considerable pressure, the case was eventually dropped before it reached court. Had court proceedings gone ahead Derek would have been in a very poor position to defend himself. A sign language interpreter would not have been any help because he was unable to sign. He would have been unable to give an articulate description and explanation of events, but would have been restricted to answering 'yes' or 'no' to questions put to him.

Possible reactions to hearing impairment as stigma

According to Goffman (1973), a central feature of the stigmatized person's life is the issue of acceptance, both by self and others. With deaf people, Furth (1973) argued that a contributing factor to their mental health is the acceptance of deafness. Whether people are accepted or not helps to shape their own self-image and self-esteem. A poor self-image and low self-esteem will be reflected in behaviour and attitudes towards both the self and others. Mead (1934) argued that we take on the views of the way others see us. If others see us as different we come to perceive ourselves as different. But different does not have to imply 'inferior'.

It is argued by Misiaszek et al (1985) that many of the personality characteristics found in deaf people may relate to methods which they use to cope with, and defend themselves against, the reactions of others and the hardships created by their handicap. There are many strategies that people can adopt in order to handle everyday interactions. For example, someone may develop a cough to explain blushing, or use humour to laugh their way out of an awkward situation (if you're a clown anything goes). There can be intellectual camouflage, where people become clever at understanding small parts of things or issues, in order to give the impression of understanding the whole. Malinowski (1927) has shown that it is possible to appear to be highly involved in social interaction when in fact little is conveyed beyond social conventions or ritualistic behaviour. By watching the reactions and gestures of others present it is possible to be involved in social interaction without having the slightest idea of what is actually said.

Coopersmith (1967) argued that, in social situations, persons who are accustomed to acceptance and expect to be successful are likely to believe that they will be treated with due appreciation of their worth; however, persons who are low in self-esteem have higher levels of anxiety, more frequent psychosomatic symptoms, are rated less effective, and are likely to be more destructive than persons who regard themselves with considerable worth.

I have developed a typology in the form of a two-by-two table to assist understanding of the ways in which hearing-impaired people can respond to their condition (see Figure 6.1). Because stigma is a social phenomenon, and also an ongoing dynamic process (as is socialization), the possible reactions are not static but need to be considered as a continuum of behaviour. People may interchange between categories depending on the circumstances involved.

Possibly the two most important factors concerning the concept of stigma are awareness and self-esteem. Awareness includes self-awareness (and self in relation to other) and other-awareness. These lie on a continuum from

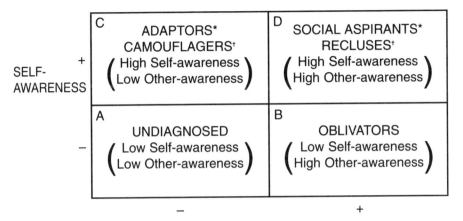

Key:
AWARENESS   SELF-ESTEEM
High Awareness +   * High = Social Progressors
Low Awareness −   † Low = Isolationists

Figure 6.1   Possible reactions to hearing impairment as stigma

non-awareness through to total awareness. Self-esteem also lies on a continuum from low to high. Both of these factors, awareness and self-esteem, are discrete, and each will play a part in the way a person reacts to hearing loss.

There are four categories – A, B, C and D – and within each category, depending on levels of awareness and self-esteem, a range of behaviours can occur on a continuum from full acceptance through to total rejection of the hearing impairment.

Categories A and B

Categories A and B are mainly concerned with the aspect of awareness.

Category A: undiagnosed

In category A there is both low self-awareness and low other-awareness that a hearing impairment exists. For example, this might include:

- an infant who is not yet diagnosed as having a hearing impairment, where the parents are unaware that there is a problem and treat the child normally;

- a child with a mild, undiagnosed hearing loss who is apparently coping in a normal-hearing setting;
- elderly people whose hearing is beginning to deteriorate, where they are not yet aware of it.

In this situation, if neither the individual nor other is aware that a potentially stigmatizing condition exists, the individual will continue to act in a 'normal' manner and will be treated accordingly by other members of society.

This category could also include situations such as the one that existed in Martha's Vineyard, an island off the southeastern coast of Massachusetts, where during the 1800s approximately 1 in 5 of the residents were deaf, and the hearing population learned sign language to communicate with them (Groce 1982). A similar example is given by Farb (1977), who during the 1960s studied a group of 500 Urubu Indians in an isolated jungle in the Amazon basin, where sign language had been developed to accommodate a deaf minority in their community. In both of these examples, the use of sign language was a normal part of the everyday environment for both hearing and deaf people from early childhood. When all members of a community can communicate easily, there need be no discrimination between members on the grounds of language ability, and therefore, because deaf people are accepted and fully integrated into that society, awareness of the self as different from the majority need not exist.

Category B: oblivators

In category B there is low self-awareness but high other-awareness that a hearing impairment exists. I have termed the people in this category 'oblivators' because it is obvious to other people that there is a hearing loss, but people in this group are oblivious to it in themselves. Many deaf children are also born with additional handicaps (Markides 1983) and, for example, children with severe learning difficulties may be unaware of their hearing loss. This category might also include deaf/blind infants or young children, or persons suffering from certain severe forms of mental illness who also have a hearing loss. The majority of people in this category are likely to be cared for by others, either in their own homes or in residential settings.

Categories C and D

Categories C and D are very much involved with both awareness and self-esteem. I have termed people with high self-esteem 'social progressors', and those with low self-esteem 'isolationists', to suggest the two extremes of a continuum, where people might try to isolate themselves as a result of the hearing loss, or openly display the fact that they are deaf. Categories C and D involve levels of awareness of hearing impairment by self and other, as well as levels of self-esteem. Taking these factors into account, the people in these two categories have various choices as to how they will react in a social situation.

Category C: adaptors or camouflagers

Category C involves people with high self-awareness of a hearing impairment, but low other-awareness. For example, a person who has become deaf post-lingually but who has clear speech might fit into this category.

Depending on whether they are social progressors or isolationists, people in this category can behave in ways which may hide the fact that they have a hearing loss, or they may adapt to a particular situation. According to the kind of behaviour they display, I have termed them either 'adaptors' or 'camouflagers'.

Adaptors will accept that a hearing impairment exists, but will alter or adapt their lifestyle so as to accommodate the loss and minimize its disadvantages as far as possible. Higgins (1980) has argued that deaf people do not necessarily view their impairment as a loss. By adapting their behaviour they are meeting people half-way.

An example of an adaptor might include the tutor in one signing class attended by the author. There was genuine surprise from some students in the class when, several weeks into the course, the tutor mentioned that she was profoundly deaf. Having been deafened post-lingually her Welsh accent and intonation were virtually unimpaired, and with excellent lip reading skills she had kept so well abreast of class discussions that her deafness had not been observed by some students.

On the other hand, if self-esteem is low, a person may experience their disability as more noticeable than it actually is. Whereas adaptors will try to minimize the disadvantages of a hearing impairment, camouflagers will try to minimize the fact that a hearing impairment exists. This could lead to overcompensation, or to avoidance of situations which might bring the hearing impairment to light. 'Invisible' hearing aids are widely advertised in the press, and advertisers can appear to be more concerned about hiding the hearing loss than with the quality of the product being sold.

Category D: social aspirants or recluses

Category D involves high awareness of a hearing impairment by both self and other – for example, a prelingually profoundly deaf person with spoken language difficulties – so that in this category it is obvious to both self and other that a hearing loss is present. Again, a range of behaviour possibilities exist on a continuum from overtly asserting that there is a hearing loss through to complete isolation and withdrawal. I have termed the people with high self-esteem in this group 'social aspirants', and those with low self-esteem 'recluses'.

An example of one social aspirant is a girl who wears rainbow-coloured hearing aids with pride. This emphasizes her deafness, so that people are aware of it before they interact with her.

At the other extreme, a recluse will try to avoid contact with others. An extreme example of a recluse was given to the author by the relative of a recently deafened man. The relative described how the man had become so withdrawn following the diagnosis that he avoided all social contact. He just stayed at home in a state of depression, refusing even to talk with close friends because he found communication so difficult. This kind of extreme reaction can lead to a very lonely and isolated existence.

Other avoidance strategies can be equally drastic, and can sometimes involve the upheaval of whole families. In another example, the mother of a profoundly deaf woman with two hearing children explained:

> She [the deaf daughter] had to move from where she used to be. People were so unkind to her. When she went to collect her children from school the other children used to make fun of her because her speech is funny. In the end she just used to wait in the car. Now when she collects her children from school she stays in the car.

Life became so intolerable for this woman and her family that they were forced to move home in order to avoid the continual harassment of certain hearing people in their neighbourhood. Whereas for many parents collecting their children from school is an enjoyable form of social contact, for this young mother it became an ordeal that she dreaded each day. Her hearing children were also affected by the continual taunts of their peer group. This same woman had experienced forms of rejection all through her childhood because of her inability to communicate effectively. In another instance her mother related that, during a hospital experience:

> I found her in the corridor at the hospital crying because no one had spoken a word to her. Not even smiled or said 'hello'.

Perhaps, had her self-esteem been higher, this woman might have felt more able to make the first move in a social situation, but having experienced continual rebuffs in interaction, and with her poor language ability, making the first move involved too high a risk of further rejection. No one she met at the hospital used sign language, and she felt very isolated and lonely.

Sometimes normal-hearing people may be overtly hostile or taunting towards the hearing-impaired (as in the case of the school children above), or their behaviour may be impatient or even dismissive, as in the example given by the profoundly deaf woman who feels embarrassed when using the bank because of staff attitudes towards her (see page 86).

At other times, actions may occur because of thoughtlessness. This can sometimes happen with professionals where routine procedures are being carried out, as in the following example in a hospital delivery room:

> When I was having my first baby – when I was actually giving birth – the sister had a mask on. I didn't understand what she was saying. Then she realized and took the mask off. She gestured 'stop' and 'carry on' so it was OK.

Once the sister realized that there was a communication problem she was able to do something about it, yet often normal-hearing people are unaware of the difficulties that deaf people face. Another common practice in hospitals is for a nurse in a ward to shine a torch towards the face of a patient when trying to communicate at night. With a deaf person the light needs to shine on the face of the nurse in order for the deaf person to communicate.

There are multifarious factors which may affect self-esteem – for example, the severity of the hearing impairment and length of time the person has been aware of it; the way in which it was acquired; the physical state of the person; whether or not other disabilities exist; personal characteristics; emotional state; ethnicity; the amount of support received from relatives, friends and colleagues, and financial resources. However, according to Coopersmith (1967), it is parents, siblings and peers who are the major defining influences on self-esteem.

Coopersmith argued that parental acceptance has an enhancing effect upon self-esteem in particular and psychosocial development in general. Rejecting parents are hostile, cold and disapproving of their children, and attitudes of disapproval may be expressed as either passive or active forms of rejection. Passive rejection involves a casual, indifferent attitude in which the child is ignored, while active rejection includes declarations of dislike, punishment, deprivation of physical necessities and social attention. Both forms express disinterest, disapproval and distaste for the child. He further argued that the parental, self and social expectations of individuals with low self-esteem are marked by lack of faith, expectations of failure, and the anticipation of rejection. By relating to their children in a distant and rejecting manner, these parents lead their children to believe that they cannot learn, are not important, and have no powers or privileges. These children come to believe that this is their due, and that they may expect similar treatment from other persons. Expectations of failure and rejection by parents thus engender doubts of adequacy in the child, which are made self-fulfilling by the manner in which the parent treats them, and the self-image of weakness and inferiority they develop.

On the other hand, 'where parents are realistic and knowledgeable about their children we would expect that a beneficient cycle of parental expectations of success leads to a child's confidence and more frequent successes, which in turn leads to greater expectations of success on his part' (Coopersmith 1967, p.251).

Many deaf students seem to develop poor self-esteem and derogatory attitudes towards themselves (Schein 1980; Meadow 1980; Schlesinger and Meadow 1972). Meadow (1980) found that deaf children of deaf parents felt more positive about themselves than did those with normal-hearing parents, and also that 'deaf children with hearing parents, who attend residential schools, have less positive self-concepts than their cohorts at day schools' (p.97).

According to Hart (1985) it is well recognized that the self-esteem of the child in school is a crucial factor in learning at all levels of success, while Brill (1976) has argued that a component of good teaching is the development of a good self-image and continuing feeling of success. Yet examples given by deaf people of their school days suggest that the school may sometimes play a part in *reducing* self-esteem. The mother of a deaf child interviewed for the present study stated:

> They used to ignore her at school and put her at the back of the class because she signed.

This reinforces Mindel and Vernon's (1971) argument that deaf children are taught that labels associated with hearing are 'better', and so the poor self-image is perpetuated. (Other examples have been given by Holmes (1981) and Rees (1983), among many others.) In developing a sense of self we take into account the view of others. Some people will affect our self-identity and self-esteem more than others. It is the people whom we identify with and whom we feel we are like, or want to be like, that most affect our self-feelings. Initially, with a young child, this is generally parents and other close family. Children with very secure home backgrounds and high self-esteem may cope very well with a hearing impairment, but for children with low self-esteem, the risk of social isolation, depression and frustration, as well as possible behavioural difficulties, is higher than for normal-hearing children.

7 Parental concerns and professional responses

As can be seen from the previous chapters, a crucial factor linked to awareness and self-esteem is that of parental reactions towards the deaf child.

Parents and 'experts'

Figure 1.1 (see page 7) highlights some of the range of personnel that parents of a newly-diagnosed deaf child might encounter. As parents at this time are having to cope with their own emotions and adjustments from the impact of diagnosis, as well as to a range of new audiological and educational information regarding their child (Meadow 1980), it is hardly surprising that they themselves may feel confused. The situation becomes more complicated when there is also confusion between the professionals who are offering advice and guidance.

It has been argued by Hastings and Hayes (1981) that parents have basic rights of which they may not be aware, and that they should not be left in confusion but should be given information. However, none of the parents interviewed in the present study felt that they were given adequate information or support. Furthermore, in some instances there was confusion about the roles of the people with whom they were interacting.

The following examples are extracts related to the author by parents who were asked at interview about the help and information they received at the time of diagnosis and following it. They serve to illustrate both a lack of information regarding the diagnosis, and a lack of support following the diagnosis.

The first example is from the mother of a partial-hearing child (who was 2

123

years 5 months at the time of diagnosis):

> He went to [the hospital]. He had a hearing test. [The doctor] explained to me all about glue ear and then said Mark didn't have glue ear (laugh) but he said he might develop it later on but at the moment, you know, there's nothing there, he's perfectly alright ... because, I should have been told Mark could have been born deaf and that what's caused the hearing problem now was the circumstances of his birth.

This was all the information she could remember having received regarding the diagnosis, and she came to her own conclusions (rightly or wrongly) that it was difficulties at birth that were the cause of the deafness. She has been left with a sense of dissatisfaction with the health and medical professions:

> but nobody ever said there was going to be a problem. Or there might be a problem I should look out for and it wasn't on his records or anything so when I did go down there [to the clinic], thinking he had a hearing problem, I was getting brushed off. What distressed me most was that no-one said to me 'You've got to look out for these things.' If someone had said ... 'Don't worry about it too much but just keep an eye out and tell the health visitor.' But of course I couldn't tell the health visitor because I didn't know.

The second example is from the father of a profoundly deaf boy (who was aged 10 months when diagnosed):

> It was so cold. 'Your son's got nerve deafness.' We're supposed to accept it. I don't understand. I ask if he can have an operation. I don't know nothing about it. I don't know. It weren't until she got me a bit annoyed with her attitude she became a bit more sort of caring. She drew me a picture of the ear. When I asked – 'No, nothing can be done.' I got annoyed. I never understood. Then she realized I was getting annoyed. She drew this diagram. I was still none the wiser.

The above example illustrates the lack of comprehension by this parent on being given the shattering and quite unexpected news that his child was profoundly and permanently deaf. At interview he vividly recalled the event (which had occurred several years previously), and still felt anger, which was directed towards the person who had broken the news to him. The fact that this man could remember the incident so clearly, and still have such intense negative feelings about it so many years later, suggests that he had not successfully worked through the grieving process outlined by Moses (1985; see Chapter 1), and was still carrying unresolved feelings.

The following two examples are concerned with information and help received after the diagnosis had been made. The same parent from the second example explained:

We did end up with a lady used to come round after we'd seen . . . [the consultant]. Some old dear come round to the house. Brought her soppy dog with her – used to take it round with her. She was – I think – . . . [after prompt from interviewer] . . . an advisory type teacher. Just to sort of start us off on what's – what we 'ad coming like. She used to tell us what to do – all the things with an ordinary kid. She used to tell us what to do and what not to do.

This father was not very clear about the purpose of the 'advisory type teacher' and did not appear to have been impressed by her visits. (There have been several changes of advisory teacher since that time in that particular area.) The lack of clarity could have any of several possible causes. For example, she may have explained her role when the parents were in too much of a state of shock to absorb what she said, or perhaps they were not concerned with questioning her role but just accepted her as someone who came to visit. What was evident from the interview was the unresolved feelings of the parent.

The final example is from the mother of a partial-hearing girl who was well over 18 months of age when the diagnosis was made:

I wasn't really given any information. Very little help – only the peripatetic teacher. I think it would have been helpful if there could have been someone to talk to – to ask questions and to explain things but there wasn't anyone. [The peripatetic teacher] was very good but she hadn't any children of her own. She's not been trained to know about problems. For example . . . sleep problems . . .

This mother had experienced quite severe sleeping problems with her child, which were not fully resolved at the time of interview some two years after diagnosis.

From all the studies that have been undertaken in the literature, there appear to be three main areas where parents of deaf children may be in need of particular professional expertise. These include:

- counselling in relation to the deafness;
- communication;
- education.

Yet in each of these areas, discrepancies and confusion regarding their roles and decision-making in relation to deaf children were found among the various professional agencies researched.

Counselling in relation to deafness

Many authors have argued for improved counselling services for families with deaf children (for example, Denmark et al. 1979; Enright 1982; Freeman et al. 1981; Hall 1989; Altschuler 1974; Rodda and Grove 1987; Luterman 1979, 1986).

According to Rogers (1942), 'Effective counselling consists of a definitely structured, permissive relationship which allows the client to gain an understanding of himself to a degree which enables him to take positive steps in the light of his new orientation' (p.18).

Rogers cautioned that counselling may sometimes be used as a means of advising or persuading people (sometimes called 'intervention'), and that, in order for counselling to be successful, there must be an awareness of both self and other on the part of the counsellor. In a situation where there is a basic assumption that the counsellor is the one most competent to decide what are to be the goals of the individual and what are the values by which the situation is seen to be judged (that is, 'the counsellor knows best'), very little is likely to be achieved. The aim of counselling is to assist the individual to grow, so that he or she can cope with the present problem and with later problems in a better-integrated fashion.

Denmark et al (1979) set out the difference between counselling, guidance and support as they relate to the handicap of deafness. They argued that counselling is the process by which the person counselled is helped, gradually, to understand what the problem means. It is simultaneously the art and skill of listening to people, and allowing them to express themselves in order that they may see their problems more clearly. Workers who practise counselling in the area of deafness must have a thorough knowledge of human growth and behaviour as well as the dynamics of interpersonal interaction and family structures.

Guidance differs from counselling in that the person receiving the guidance is given a number of options and, through discussion, comes to decide upon certain modes of action. It also requires a knowledge of both statutory and voluntary helping services. Denmark et al claim that guidance is often confused with the giving of advice, which is a more directive form of help; the giving of advice does not proffer a choice of options.

Support can be usefully offered by almost any sympathetic individual who happens to have meaningful knowledge and understanding of the problems caused in the family by the presence of a deaf child. In a study on the families of 75 deaf adolescents, Denmark et al (1979) found that, throughout the whole of the adolescents' lives, only 24 out of 43 parents with profoundly deaf children questioned (56 per cent) had the opportunity to hold discussions with professional people on the general topic of deafness. They argued that such counselling would not only help with the management of the child, but also with adjustment of the whole family to their new and special situation. Only 12 of the 43 parents received advice about specific behaviour problems, although the majority experienced behaviour and adjustment problems.

From the results of the present study a gap in the services offered by professionals was identified. None of the parents interviewed felt that they had received counselling relating to the deafness of their children.

There is a range of professionals who could possibly offer counselling to parents with deaf children – for example, health visitors, advisory teachers, social workers, audiological personnel, hospital staff, etc. Of these, health visitors and advisory teachers appear to be most closely connected with parents of preschool hearing-impaired children, and therefore the most obvious people to offer this service, yet it seems that very few are actually doing so.

Health visitors receive a certain amount of education in counselling and interpersonal skills during their training, as well as a background in growth and development, and many go on to take further training in counselling, either independently or through in-service training.

In the present study it was found that, although 33 out of the 49 health visitors questioned (67 per cent) claimed to offer some form of support – reassurance, listening or more frequent visiting – to parents of newly-diagnosed deaf children, only 5 (10 per cent) offered specific counselling in this area.

From the sample, 35 (71 per cent) of health visitors assumed that another professional was giving this service. Out of these, 10 assumed that this service was being offered by the education department, while another 21 did not specify any particular persons or department. Two respondents suggested a social worker as performing this role, one offered 'hospital' as a response, and one offered 'audiology'.

The majority of health visitors were under the impression that specific counselling for the parents of deaf children was being provided by others. Yet, from the interviews conducted with parents, and from discussion with personnel in the education services, this was clearly not the case.

Of the health visitors who were questioned, 16 per cent specifically offered advisory teachers as the personnel within the education department who were providing this service. During an interview with the senior area adviser for special educational needs, the author was informed that counselling is not specifically a part of the role of the advisory teacher.

It was explained that advisory teachers for hearing-impaired children in this area work as part of a team which includes specialists in the areas of sensory handicap, physical handicap, preschool work, the curriculum, and children with learning difficulties. Their major role involves the guidance of parents of preschool hearing-impaired children, and advising teachers and other personnel – such as those in nurseries, opportunity classes and playgroups – in relation to hearing-impaired children. They are responsible for advising heads and class teachers of mainstream schools where there are hearing-impaired children, and they also liaise with special schools where there is a child with hearing impairment as a secondary handicap, as well as with further education colleges where applicable. At all levels they have the dual function of advising parents and teachers, and also of advising the authority in terms of provision for those children as individuals.

Enright (1982) examined some of the priorities involved in parent guidance services for families of preschool children with hearing impairment, and suggested that peripatetic advisory teachers could usefully apply counselling skills to improve the services offered to families with deaf children.

At present, counselling is not a specific part of the role of advisory teachers, and those who may wish to develop counselling skills have to train themselves. Equally, at present, the health visitors questioned in general do not see specific counselling for parents of hearing-impaired children as a part of their role, although 85 per cent of the sample said that they would welcome education and training in this aspect.

Although a small number of health visitors (10 per cent of the sample) do claim to be giving specific counselling to parents, it seems that at present the majority do not feel able to offer this service.

From discussion with audiological personnel it appears that social workers, who would seem to be the other obvious group to perform this service, rarely become involved with families following the diagnosis of a deaf child. None of the parents interviewed in the study had been visited by a social worker for the deaf. A referral is only made to the social services department if there are known to be specific social problems within a family. No evidence was found that counselling was being provided by any of the other possible professional groups who might be in a position to offer this service.

Communication choice

As has been discussed throughout the present study, the method of communication which should be used by parents with their hearing-impaired children remains an area of controversy. The two diametrically opposed views, which range from the purely oral approach through to the total signing approach, are still strongly debated.

Initially, few parents of a newly-diagnosed deaf child are likely to be aware of the oral/manual controversy, and their information must, at least to begin with, come from the 'experts' with whom they have contact. Because hearing parents have so little knowledge of the problems associated with deafness, Ladd (1979) has argued that it is not surprising that they go along with the line: 'the professional knows best'. But this assumption may not always be correct.

For example, the mother of a hearing-impaired child explained:

> I didn't know what questions to ask. I didn't know what were the normal speech levels. I now know that the audiogram hearing starts at 0 and speech starts at 25. Jane's hearing starts at 65 but I didn't know that. It would have been helpful if someone could have explained what it meant. They talk about percentage loss but I didn't know what it meant in terms of what she can and can't hear.

The professional may not give information in a way that can be understood by the parent. Equally, the professional may not possess the knowledge to be able to inform the parent.

Sometimes parents and professionals have different views because they have different priorities, experiences and sources of information (Freeman et al 1981). If the professionals with whom parents interact have strong ideas or biases towards a particular form of communication, parents are not, initially at least, in a position to offer any objection because they do not possess enough information or knowledge to raise an objection.

Research has shown that parental behaviour plays a central role in the intellectual development of children; and, according to Katz (1980), research findings are reflected in such catch-phrases as 'parents are the child's first teacher' or even its 'best' teacher (p.47).

Unfortunately there is a danger that this form of argument may be used by some professionals as a reason for opting out of professional responsibility. Although parents may potentially be their child's best teacher, with a deaf child they may need a lot of support and guidance which professionals can provide, yet all too often a tremendous amount of pressure is put onthem by professionals. For example, parents may read in the literature on deafness such statements as: 'The whole success or failure of treatment depends on the mother' (Fry 1968, p.200); or: 'whether or not the hearing-impaired child talks is the decision of his parents. With the right hearing aids, enough sound, enough looking and enough teaching he can learn to do so, but only his parents, and in particular his mother, can provide him with those things' (Courtman-Davies 1979, p.118); or: 'Parents must be made aware of their critical role in the language acquisition process' (Crandell 1978, p.385).

Such sweeping statements only add to parental guilt, and may lead to avoidance of professional responsibility. The term 'enough sound' immediately suggests that the child has the potential to hear providing that sound is channelled correctly, and implies that the parents are somehow at fault if this does not happen. Yet, as Denmark (1982) has pointed out, 'it is a myth that all deaf children have residual hearing and therefore can learn to speak' (p.70).

In general, parents expect that their children will learn to speak when they are old enough and, from investigations undertaken in this study, it would appear that this assumption remains true whether the child is deaf or hearing. It seems that only with knowledge and experience is this myth shattered. When given the statement 'All deaf children could learn to speak if enough time and effort was put into teaching them', a significant difference was found between teachers of the deaf and all the other groups tested (see Figure 7.1).

Of the teachers of the deaf, 67 per cent disagreed with this statement, compared with 16 per cent of the general public and 13 per cent of parents of not-yet-tested children. Only 11 per cent of teachers of the deaf agreed with this statement compared with 50 per cent of the general public and 59 per cent of parents of not-yet-tested children (see Figure 7.1). Of the school children who were tested, when taken as total samples within each school at the first testing, 9 per cent of children with experience of partial hearing (PHE) and the control group (PC), and 18 per cent of children with experience of signers (SE) and the control group (SC), disagreed with the statement. In both groups the agree response was 65 per cent (see Figure 7.1). Figure 7.2 shows a breakdown of the school children divided into classes, and into the first and second testing for 'agree' and 'disagree' responses. As previously stated, the first testing was carried out at the very start of the school year, before the children in the SE group had met their profoundly deaf peers (the children in the PHE group had already met their classmate). It was expected that, at this stage, results would be similar to those of the general public. The second testing, however, was carried out at the end of the same school year, following both exposure to hearing-impaired peers and an educational input from teachers of the deaf who explained some of the problems associated with hearing loss. (This took place in both schools, with different teachers of the deaf.)

Although the differences observed between the first and second testings were not statistically significant, interestingly the 'agree' responses dropped in all classes except for the PHE group. The SE group fell from 71 per cent to 55 per cent and the SC group from 60 per cent to 48 per cent; while the PHC group fell from 73 per cent to 67 per cent. However, 'agree' responses in the PHE group rose from 58 per cent to 63 per cent. This may reflect the differences in experience between the groups. The partial-hearing child whom that group experienced had extremely good speech and was well integrated into the school system, whereas the PHC group in that school had no experience of hearing impairment beyond what they learned from a talk by a teacher of the deaf. The SE children were more exposed to children with poor speech intelligibility, and had regular on-going talks by teachers of the deaf, which would have raised their knowledge and awareness. Another

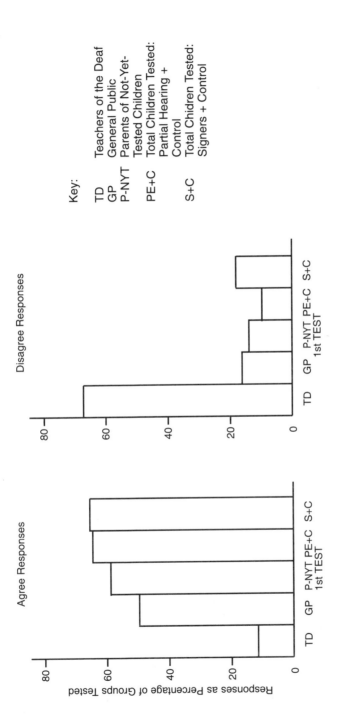

Figure 7.1 Responses to the statement: 'All deaf children could learn to speak if enough time and effort was put into teaching them'

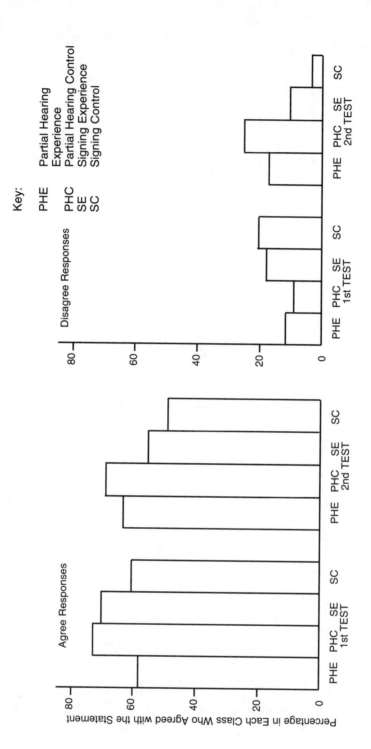

Figure 7.2 Responses of school children to the statement: 'All deaf children could learn to speak if enough time and effort was put into teaching them'

interesting (but non-significant) observation was that in both the PHE and PHC groups the 'disagree' responses rose at the second testing, while in the SE and SC groups they dropped (in favour of 'don't know' responses). It would seem that by the end of the school year the children in the school with signers were less sure about some of their responses in relation to their profoundly deaf peers.

So there is an assumption by lay people that children will learn to speak if given enough time and effort. Teachers of the deaf, however, with their knowledge and experience of hearing impairment, are more aware of the reality. Studies have shown that speech development and speech intelligibility depend on a large number of factors, and that, no matter how much input and effort is made, some profoundly deaf children do not learn to speak (for example, Quigley and Paul 1984; Markides 1985, 1986; Mindel and Vernon 1971; Vernon 1969; Montgomery 1976; Rodda and Grove 1987).

Montgomery (1981a) has argued that too often parents are told that their deaf child is the same as any other child, and that parents may be ashamed of the deafness, or may want to pretend that their child is not deaf. Denmark (1976) has pointed out that most parents of young deaf children are naturally only too ready to listen to the advice of pure oralists not to use manual methods of communication. Yet his experience of working with deaf adolescents and their families has demonstrated that they eventually come to realize that the advice given was quite unrealistic and grossly optimistic.

Decisions about communication need to be made as soon as possible after the diagnosis of hearing impairment has been made. These decisions are very much in the hands of the professionals. If, as has been found in the present study, parents expect that their child can and will learn to speak, they may be reluctant to consider the possibility of learning sign language if the need arises. Parental responses to sign language are likely to depend on what they are told by professionals.

There was a general consensus among both the lay public and teachers of the deaf that sign language is a proper language (see Figure 5.2, page 95), yet there are many factors to be considered and taken into account on this issue.

Higgins (1980) has argued that sign makes deaf people visible, and therefore can make them discredited in the eyes of hearing people. If self-esteem is low, some children may reject sign because they do not want to appear to be different. According to Ladd (1979), for hearing parents, to be oral is to be normal. To be normal is to deny deafness. To deny deafness is to relieve our own guilt and discomfort at having to face up to deafness; while Mindel and Vernon (1971) have argued that parents are conditioned to regard manual programmes as a sign of failure, which then affects the whole personality of the child (see also Montgomery 1981a). They have pointed out that parents are given slogans and sayings, such as: 'Every child deserves a chance at oralism', and 'If a child is taught sign language he will never learn to talk' (p.72), although there is no evidence to support these views.

Although Mindel and Vernon were writing over two decades ago, similar views are still very much in evidence today. For example, Tweedie (1987) has stated that:

> There is no universally recognised sign language but many of the signs are based on ideas or pictures. It is surprising how subtle and speedy the use of this method can become but it is still, of course, far slower and clumsier than speech and its lack of universality and of comprehension by the normal hearing render it a cumbersome and often unrewarding exercise (p.77)

while Rosenbloom (1987) claimed that 'The majority of deaf children have limited or abnormal speech and frequently their problems extend to writing and signing – which are also limited in linguistic terms' (p.130).

Such comments show a distinct lack of awareness of the true nature of both sign language and language in general. There is no single universally recognized language at all, although attempts have been made with spoken language (Esperanto), and also with sign language. According to Montgomery (1981b), 'Gestuno' is a compromise language widely accepted as the international sign system used as an auxiliary language at committees and conferences. It contains vocabulary from BSL, Ameslan, Scandinavian, Latin languages and East European sources, with many other indigenous systems contributing. It was developed by the World Federation of the Deaf and the United Nations, has been compiled in a well-structured photographic dictionary by the British Deaf Association, and is circulated widely throughout the world (Montgomery, 1981b, p.1). As for sign language being slower than speech, Brennan (1989) has shown that, with BSL, in some instances it is possible to convey several concepts with one movement, and when attempting to translate from BSL to English, it is English, she maintains, which turns out to be the more clumsy language.

There are certain important considerations to be taken into account over the question of whether or not hearing parents should learn sign language. According to Swisher and Thompson (1985), hearing mothers are not immersed in a culture of signing adults, they are immersed in the culture of their first language, with little exposure to sign; and they usually only get a small amount of teaching (generally one to two hours per week), and in general only sign with their deaf child. Gregory and Barlow (1986) have argued that, because it is not the mother tongue, the signing spoken by the family is not the same as sign language used by most deaf families. Because there is evidence to suggest that fathers frequently don't learn sign beyond the beginners stage (Bornstein et al 1980), and that the whole family may not participate in learning sign, the mother and child may become isolated in their own communication system. Also, parents may experience difficulty in finding signing classes (Denmark et al 1979; Rodda and Grove 1987), or in gaining signing experience with deaf adults (Brennan 1989).

Learning sign language involves the parents in learning a new language, yet Moeller and Luetke-Stahlman (1990) agreed with Swisher and Thompson (1985) that traditional ways of teaching sign are ill-designed to meet the needs of parents. Parents need to learn signing skills, and they also need assistance to learn to apply those skills to facilitate the language development of their child. Often deaf children will overtake their parents in sign vocabulary growth once they are signing in the school setting, which may reduce the parents' confidence in their own signing ability. Yet, as discussed previously, there is considerable evidence demonstrating the problems that may arise if no adequate means of communication is found.

According to J.C. Denmark (1982), there is no evidence to support the argument that deaf children who learn sign language won't be motivated to learn lip reading and speech skills, while C. Denmark (1990) cited evidence from Denmark, where a group of deaf children who began their education using the medium of Danish Sign Language (DSL), by the age of 12 years were asking for their lessons to be given in spoken Danish, having mastered DSL as their first language.

The oralist emphasis on lip reading gives some cause for concern. Comments such as the following from Dale (1972) – 'If parents build up a good set of pictures to help their child to learn to lip read, there is often little need to resort to gestures', which is endorsed by Tweedie (1987): 'it is not generally realised that 50 per cent of spoken language can be perceived by vision alone' (p.80) (which contradicts the research: see Chapter 3, page 40) – help to perpetuate the idea that all deaf children can and will learn to speak, and that lip reading skill is relatively easily acquired. Yet, as Mindel and Vernon (1971) have argued, a blind child learns language at the same time as a normal-hearing child without looking at mouth patterns, and lip reading is not a normal part of acquiring language. Denmark (1982) pointed out that, not only is lip reading extremely difficult, it also presupposes a knowledge of verbal language (which young deaf children do not possess); while Davis (1976) has made the point that children cannot lip read at functions such as school assemblies and prizegivings, and that it puts an unfair strain on the children (see Chapter 3, page 39).

Davis (1976) has also argued that it is a myth, held by hearing people, that it is not possible to sign and lip read together. People can and do. This view is endorsed by many people (perhaps mainly those who happen to be fluent in both sign language and English) working with deaf children. The myth itself highlights another factor which has already been raised – the proficiency of signing educators, and the question of whether or not deaf children should be educated bilingually. Moores et al (1972) found that Total Communication has no adverse effects upon the acquisition of oral skills, and does not detract from a child's ability to utilize residual hearing, while Denmark (1982) argued: 'indeed all the evidence tends to suggest the opposite view – that combined manual and oral methods should be employed from the earliest years – years when a meaningful form of communication is so vitally important for future intellectual, social and emotional development' (p.70). This is supported by Rodda and Grove (1987) with their review of the literature.

Another point on this issue, made by Montgomery (1986b), is that 'The vast majority of sign language users bring up their hearing children to use sign language and among the several hundred of these the present writer has met throughout the world, there is not one whose speech was in any way retarded because of their use of sign' (p.49). Confirming this view, a study by Schiff-Myers and Klein (1985) of the speech of normal-hearing children of deaf parents, compared with children from normal-speaking homes, found that the phonological processes used were the same as those among children from hearing homes. None adopted the less typical productions found in the speech of their deaf parents.

Education

According to Denmark et al (1979), education begins at home but, in the case of the deaf child, social and behavioural education cannot begin until effective parent–child communication is established. Mindel and Vernon (1971) have argued that, in the last analysis, it is parents and not the professionals who have the responsibility for the child's destiny, but also that the deaf child is almost completely under the control of the educators, and that deaf children are captive to the system. If these statements are true then parents of deaf children would appear to be in the contradictory position of carrying total responsibility for their child, but with no control over decisions that are made concerning the child.

How much information do parents actually receive, and how much are they really able to choose? Over and above the understandable general feeling of wanting more information, which most parents of a newly-diagnosed child with a disability experience, all the parents of deaf children interviewed for the present study felt that they did not receive enough information (this included areas of the deafness itself, communication, voluntary agencies, and education). The following are some examples of comments made to the author during interviews:

Till the kid gets into school you don't get to know too much.

I wasn't told about any agencies. I contacted the BDA myself because I was interested in learning BSL, but at the time there were no local classes running.

> I wasn't put in touch with any voluntary agencies. It's only that the NDCS organizer for this area came to talk at one of our meetings, collecting up names, so I gave her ours and now we get the regular magazine they send out to the parents of deaf children.

With the parents of deaf children interviewed for the present study, it was established that the question of educational choice was not raised by the professionals with whom they had contact. This could be because – although in theory, following the Education Act 1981, parental choice is now a consideration in educational placement – in reality, because of financial and other constraints, the choice is extremely limited (for example, there is only one primary school for deaf children in the geographical area where the research was conducted).

The father of a profoundly deaf boy recounted to the author his experience over the educational placement for his son:

> I remember we had to go – we had to go and see this lady who was grim. The gist was John would be needing some school. This lady was concerned that meself and me missus wouldn't want John to come to a deaf school. She was trying to give us the impression of how badly deaf he was and he'd never get on at an ordinary school.

In this example there was no question of choice. It was a matter of the professional persuading the parents that a particular school was best for their child.

As part of the present study the author was concerned with how educational decisions are made, by whom, and how much choice parents actually have in that process. Interviews were conducted with the senior area adviser for special educational needs, and the head of the audiological service. As found with all the professionals interviewed in the present study, the most striking aspect from these two interviews was the strong sense of caring and commitment that came across from both of these people, and their belief that they were acting in the best interests of the children with whom they worked. However, as will be discussed, differences were found between them which have implications for children with hearing impairment and their parents.

Educational provision for deaf children in this area begins as soon as the diagnosis is made, not as direct teaching but as guidance to parents to assist their child to begin to acquire language and speech. This work is undertaken by advisory teachers, and preschool work is normally done in children's homes.

From the audiological side it was ascertained that any child with a hearing aid is automatically put in contact with an advisory teacher. That teacher then follows the child through school and makes decisions if they feel that the child is not coping educationally. It is the advisory teacher who decides whether the child should attend a partial-hearing unit, a school for the deaf, or mainstream schooling. The clinic used to be more involved in educational decisions, but now it is the education department that makes the decisions.

However, a different view was advanced by the education department, where, in keeping with the Education Act 1981, a statement is drawn up by all the people involved with the child. Once assessment has been made and educational needs determined, then it becomes the job of the authority to match needs to provision. Where there is any choice in the matter, then parents can discuss their feelings. At the stage when we know pretty precisely what the needs are, there is not a great range of choice in the provision.

A parent may want to say: 'I don't want my child to go to a special school' – and there can be problems when a parent doesn't want that school. The parents can object, but there is no real choice. If we can't find common ground then the authority issues a statement and the parent needs to appeal. With markedly hearing-impaired children, the advisory teacher will usually have been working with the parents for two or three years before the final assessment, and will have helped the parents to appreciate the child's needs. It is very rare to have a conflict.

Note

1   For further information see Rogers (1977, 1987) for discussion on client-centered therapy, and Nelson-Jones (1982) and Patterson (1986) for a theoretical background of counselling and psychotherapy.

8 Summary and conclusions

Part I of this book has considered some of the issues which are current in the field of deafness, particularly focusing on the areas of diagnosis, education, and integration, and how they may affect and be affected by the socialization process. How a deaf child is socialized is intricately linked to communication, therefore I have argued that, although these are apparently separate areas, they cannot be considered in isolation because each has such a profound effect on the others.

From a detailed survey of the literature it appears that some of the issues have altered very little over the past hundred years. Although toned down somewhat, the oral/manual controversy is still being debated; the deaf still have poor speech development and low educational achievement, with little prospect of gaining professional employment, and there is still confusion and conflict within and among the various professions operating within this field. This in turn leads to confusion for parents, and thus for the child.

From the present study it was found that the attitudes of professionals at the time of diagnosis are likely to have major implications for parents and their hearing-impaired children. These attitudes may affect:

- the way in which parents react to the initial diagnosis of deafness in their children;
- whether parents work through a grieving process and come to terms with the hearing loss;
- parental acceptance or rejection of their children;
- the form of communication that those children will use;
- the education of those children;
- ultimately, the self-esteem of those children.

These points can be considered under the two main headings of diagnosis and communication.

Diagnosis

The manner in which parents are told of the diagnosis of their child can affect how they act towards that child. What they believe the child is capable of achieving will stem from what they are told at the time of diagnosis, and is likely to affect responses in the child. Responses in the child will in turn affect parental reactions, and a cycle of interaction is set up which will affect the socialization of that child.

Hearing parents undergo a diagnostic crisis, during which they may receive conflicting professional advice which can leave them anxious, stressed and overwhelmed.

The impact of diagnosis must not be underestimated, no matter how calmly parents may appear to receive the news and react to it initially. Luterman (1979) has observed that 'when hearing loss is diagnosed in their child hearing parents become angry, which leads to rejection and despair; and the child may experience rejection and feel that he is the source of the parents' despair' (p.18). From earlier child development studies it is known that 'When parents' attitudes are rejecting of children, children show a slightly decelerated intellectual development, relatively poor use of the abilities they do possess, and some lack of originality. They are emotionally unstable, rebellious, aggressive and quarrelsome' (Rogers 1942, p.77). Deaf children have enough difficulties to overcome without the additional burden of parental rejection through unresolved grief.

An example of parental rejection has been given (see page 59) where a mother resorted to physical violence and denial of food for her profoundly deaf daughter for not pronouncing words correctly (even though the child did not understand them). The little girl had been deafened by meningitis at 3 years of age and it is likely that the mother never came to terms with the hearing loss in her daughter.

It has been argued by Meadow and Meadow (1971) that people become parents – that is, they generally learn ways of behaving and seeing the self in a given role – but that having a disabled child may be seen as an unwanted and distasteful status. The majority of hearing parents live in a hearing world and expect that their child will grow up to do the same. Among others, Bloom (1965) has pointed out that, with a congenitally deaf child, initially it is the hearing parents who suffer, not the child – who is unlikely to be aware of any particular difference between self and others (that awareness develops later).

The fact that deaf parents do not view the diagnosis of deafness in their child as the same kind of disaster that hearing parents do (Meadow 1980) suggests that there may be an element imposed by the hearing society which affects the non-hearing's status. Apart from their own feelings, parents also have to contend with the reactions of relatives, friends and neighbours, and may experience the stigma of having a child who is 'different from us'. For example, the father of a profoundly deaf boy explained:

> I get really pissed off with my family – my mother – 'cos they ain't made much effort to get involved with the old boy much. We don't live close and that, but in the early stages with him – If one of me brothers had had John I'd support him . . . But with me mother you wonder if it must have been something you said 'cos it caused a lot of gripe. He weren't an accident. Think they might have thought 'It serves you bleedin' right. That's what you get for having another kid.'

Another important factor to be considered is that of the effect of cultural differences on the reactions of parents and others towards a child diagnosed as deaf. For example, in the Yoruba culture in Nigeria there is a relationship between sin and handicap. In the case of a congenitally handicapped child, the handicap reflects the sins of either the parents of the child or close relatives. Depending on the beliefs about the cause of deafness, reactions may be either accepting (Olubanji 1981) or rejecting (Togonu-Bickersteth and Odebiyi 1985). Parents may experience a sense of embarrassment or shame, and not want to admit to having a deaf child.

The importance of acceptance is a theme which runs continuously through counselling literature, as well as through the literature concerning deaf children (for example, Reed 1956, cited in Ballantyne 1970; Jones 1986), along with the fact that, until deafness is accepted, progress is impeded. (The concept of acceptance is expanded later in this chapter.)

Communication

Negative attitudes towards manual communication implant the idea of 'oral failures' from the time of diagnosis. Schlesinger (1986) has argued that, once a child has experienced a sense of failure, there is likely to be parent–child failure, and quite possibly teacher–child failure, and that a sense of powerlessness is evoked in the parents by a hearing-impaired child (Schlesinger 1985). I have argued that a sense of powerlessness is also evoked in the parents by the professionals with whom they have initial contact.

In the present study it was found that major decisions concerning the mode of communication to be used tended to be made at the time of diagnosis. From talking with parents of deaf children a pattern began to emerge. Several parents explained that, because of a lack of knowledge or prior experience about deafness, they were ignorant of any alternatives, and did not know what questions to ask, therefore they were in the hands of the 'experts' and had to take any information given to them on trust.

In the geographical area studied, there appeared to be a strong consensus of opinion among the professionals in this field that speech was the mode of communication to be aimed for, and that sign language was very much second best. The bias towards speech came across strongly from both the educational and the audiological personnel interviewed. Although there is no actual communication policy, the emphasis was very much on speech, and although Signed English was used in education as part of a Total Communication approach, it was only considered as an aid to learning spoken English, whilst BSL was not considered at all; and, although the audiological physician (who headed the audiological service in the area) was not opposed to sign language, again the preference was very much for the acquisition of speech. At interview it was explained that:

> I believe in using every available method, but let's try to teach them to talk first. Encourage speech first, but if it's not coming, for example by the time they get to 5, or younger if they are severely deaf, then bring in signing. If you encourage signing too early then they will not bother so much about speech. They can learn signing later. It's incredible how much speech a severely deaf child can have.

This bias towards speech was confirmed by interviews with parents of deaf children. For example, one mother explained:

> They basically said speech is best. There can be a need for sign for very deaf children and deaf parents in families, but it doesn't act as a substitute for speech.

In the following example, the experience described by the mother of a profoundly deaf boy is by no means unique:

> After the diagnosis the peripatetic teacher told us not to sign. We were told 'Don't use your hands'. The booklet we were given also said 'Don't use your hands'. We asked for more information and then we got the NDCS reading list – after reading the book by Mindel and Vernon [1971] we decided we wanted to use signing, but there were no sign language classes available. We got opposition from the doctor who diagnosed the deafness; the ear mould technician; the teacher of the deaf, and the health visitor. We insisted on using sign language for our child. We wanted him to be taught in sign language. Eventually we got to see the head of the education department. The educational psychologist had recommended [school] and they had agreed, but then because of the high cost of education they tried to back out.

Eventually this child did attend a signing school, instead of the partial-hearing unit which the education authority had tried to insist on, and both parents were able to learn sign language, but they had to battle with the authorities every step of the way. Other parents who are perhaps less articulate or determined may be less inclined or likely to question 'expert' opinion. Indeed, the majority of parents interviewed for the present study appeared simply to accept the professional opinions given to them under the assumption that 'they know best'.

From the interviews undertaken it appears that, in general, decisions about the mode of communication to be used tend to be made by failing to mention that there are alternative possibilities, rather than denying parents the right to use sign language with their child outright. In several instances it was only when parents decided independently that they wanted sign language for their child that the question was raised, and then it was raised by the parents. Even then, professionals can convey disapproval, which can leave a parent feeling guilty. For example, one mother informed the author that:

We felt concern at the start by wanting sign for our child. Were we stopping Alan from learning to speak?

In other instances the decision to use sign was made at the time of educational placement (that is, when the child was approximately $2^1/_2$–3 years of age), when it became apparent that speech was not progressing. For some parents this was the first they knew about sign language. For example, the father of a profoundly deaf boy explained:

John was gone $2^1/_2$ when he started at the deaf school. $2^1/_2$ to 3 anyway. It was before he was 3. This school – that's the first dealings with signing. We came for three days. For the three-day course. I don't think they do it anymore? That's where we first met [a profoundly deaf sign language teacher at the school]. When I met her – I sort of like – when you meet a deaf person who can talk and can understand, for the first time – it gives you a lot of hope like.

This child had already lost nearly three years of language development before the question of signing arose. In the following example, the child was 7 years old before sign language was introduced:

We didn't know what to expect. We'd never had a deaf child before. Peter went to a partial hearing unit ... because there was no special school available where he lived. He reached $6^1/_2$ to 7 years before we realized he wasn't getting anywhere. We had terrible problems at home – he got frustrated and used to cry a lot. We got frustrated and angry – because of the behaviour problems and tension etcetera. We made up our own signs – it was the only way to communicate with him. Eventually he changed to [a school for deaf children] and we found many of our signs were the same as they use at school. There's already a difference in him – but he's a late starter – he's missed seven years. Neighbours and close friends said 'Oh good! Now he has his hearing aids he'll be OK.' They didn't understand that in Peter's case they make virtually no difference.

All the evidence in the literature points to the need for signing to begin as early as possible in order to encourage language development. Yet, at least in the area studied for this book, this is clearly not happening. Parents of a newly-diagnosed child are not generally in a position to question professional advice because they are unaware either of issues in the field of deafness or of the implications for the profoundly deaf child of not learning sign language.

Professional conflicts and confusion

One of the major findings of the present study has been that the attitudes of professionals have had a marked effect on the attitudes and behaviour of parents, which in turn has affected the way they perceive and react to their children, and hence the socialization of those children.

Comments made to parents at the time of diagnosis can have far-reaching implications for the future of that child. Although these findings came independently as a result of the present study, since they were made, supporting references by others have been discovered. For example, Rodda and Grove (1987) state that:

> shocking though it may seem, a second possible explanation is that deaf children are, at least in this context, negatively affected by specialist intervention. Interview data describing lack of support and the lack of good counselling given to parents by official agencies, at the time of diagnosis and subsequently, are not inconsistent with this explanation. (p.318)

Likewise, Denmark et al (1979) concluded that one of the most significant findings of their study was the lack of psychological and social work support received by the families, even though the families had been in contact with health, educational and social services for many years. When asked why they did not receive help, 'the most frequent response was that they had never realised that such support was available or that they had never been approached. Very few parents felt that such help was not necessary, and clearly in the light of the problems described, it would almost certainly have been beneficial' (p.76). Freeman et al (1981) have set out what they consider to be the characteristics of a 'good professional': these include seeing people as individuals; being available and dependable; being honest about personal limitations and mistakes; being willing to change an opinion when presented with new facts, and being able to explain decisions, policies and technical terms so that parents can understand them.

Following the interviews with parents of deaf children in the present study, it seems that, at times, some of these characteristics were not always at the forefront of the interactions. Parents were not always aware of the professional identity of the people with whom they were interacting, or of the purpose of the interaction.

After many interviews with professionals in this field and parents of deaf children, it became clear that there was confusion among professionals as to who actually makes the decisions regarding the method of communication to be used by the child and the form of education they will receive. A lot of the responsibility appeared to rest with the advisory teachers. For example, one mother informed me that:

> The decision about signing depends very much on what the advisory teacher thinks. If everyone agrees it's OK ... We got our information from the advisory teacher – we see her weekly. We only see the audiologist monthly or so,

while the senior area adviser for special educational needs advised me that:

> There is no occasion when signing is decided in complete isolation. This should be a joint decision,

but then added later:

> Where there is a reasonable degree of likelihood that the child will need additional help, some advisory teachers might introduce signing at the preschool stage,

which appears to contradict the first statement. He also added that advisory teachers are not required to have any training in sign language, although some may put themselves on courses from choice. If an advisory teacher is not conversant with sign language, the question then arises, how is sign language being introduced to parents?

As mentioned in Chapter 7 (pages 137–8), a difference of opinion existed between the educational and audiological departments concerning school placement, with the education department maintaining that it was a joint decision, and the audiology department claiming that it was a purely educational decision. Again, it is the advisory teacher who is most involved with the child, and is therefore likely to have a major role in that decision-making process.

General confusion and disagreement among professionals leads to confusion for parents, and eventually confusion for the child.

What did become apparent from the present study was the lack of choice that parents have in any of the decisions concerning their children – this has also been found by other researchers (for example, Mindel and Vernon 1971; Luterman 1979) – and also a lack of awareness by the majority of parents that there might be any choices to be made. Rather than having any choice, decisions about communication methods and education were made by professionals and the parents informed as a *fait accompli*.

The findings of this study suggest that deaf children and their parents have (unwittingly) been oppressed by caring and responsible professionals who sincerely believe that they are acting in the best interests of those children. As mentioned in Chapter 7 (page 137), a deep sense of caring and commitment was apparent from all the professionals interviewed for this study, each wanting the best possible outcome for those children. It appears that, at the same time, each was falling into the trap of viewing the situation from too narrow a perspective, rather than considering a more holistic approach. There is a danger of complacency, of not reviewing what is actually happening.

Sign language is not the preferred mode of communication for every hearing-impaired child (although this policy is beginning to be adopted in other countries – for example, in Denmark: Hansen 1987) and nor is a signing education. But, as Mindel and Vernon (1971) have argued, parents are ultimately responsible for their children and should be included in the decision-making process. In order to be included they need to be given information and the opportunity for discussion.

Recommendations

Throughout the interviews undertaken for the present study, a major concern was the lack of professional help received by parents, both in terms of a lack of information and a lack of support. This supports Tumin (1978, cited in Webster and Wood 1989, p.29), who found that the three most frequent sources of complaint by parents are: inadequate information, unrealistic advice, and not listening to what parents themselves have to say.

Parents have very little possibility, immediately after a diagnosis of hearing loss has been made in their child, of getting information other than from the professionals with whom they come into contact. They need to feel able to trust the 'experts' who are treating their child and to rely on the information that is given to them. While it is important not to devastate them further, the information given should be appropriate to the situation and, as far as possible, supported by reliable research evidence. Very few prelingually profoundly deaf children grow up to be musicians. Fantasies about future expectations and hopes may have to be altered or replaced.

The Hall Report (Hall 1989) states that 'parents should be treated as equal partners in child health care' (p.88), and it emphasizes the important role of parents in detecting and acknowledging the possibility of developmental problems. Yet, all too often, parental concerns are ignored.

Luterman (1979) has argued that parents go to professionals with many expectations, some of which may not be met. Professionals need to be able to work with feelings. If parents feel that they do not have enough support, this may not reflect the actual physical amount of support being given or offered. If professionals appear 'cold' or try to remain detached and objective, and do not reach the emotional side of parents, then change within those parents is unlikely to take place.

It has been argued by Cumming (1982, cited in Rodda and Grove 1987, p.309) that the outcome of counselling is acceptance. I consider that it is through the process of acceptance that change is facilitated. It is the mutual, empathic 'touching', on an emotional level, of two people which facilitates a process that enables change to come about, so that change actually occurs through acceptance: being accepted by another, and accepting the present situation.

Therefore I will add my voice to the steadily growing stream of authors in this field who are expounding the need for counselling (see Chapter 7) for hearing parents following the diagnosis of hearing impairment in their child.

There is a need for a person trained in counselling, as part of a multidisciplinary team, to liaise with all the other personnel involved with the family, with the specific role of helping the family through the diagnostic crisis (this is expanded below).

There needs to be a multidisciplinary team approach, with good liaison between its members who work with the family from hearing screening through to school-leaving age and beyond where necessary, with a different emphasis on different professionals as the need arises. Such teams are already in operation in areas such as Manchester and Nottingham (see, for example, Webster et al 1985, cited in Webster and Wood 1989).

In order to be able to handle emotions in their clients, professionals need to be able to cope with emotions within themselves. They need to learn how to handle the negative reactions of parents without taking the guilt or blame onto themselves. This requires training and experience. There is a need for a team approach to give support to all its members, so that parents themselves may be supported.

A common reaction when given an unwanted diagnosis is for parents to turn against the professional who has given the bad news, so there needs to be back-up support, both for the rejected professional and for the parents. A flexible approach is also needed so that parents do not get caught up in a bureaucratic system where they feel overwhelmed and alone. They need a positive, supportive environment. This can be enhanced by regular meetings between professionals, and also between parents and professionals.

There is a need for a separate specialist person to take on the role of facilitator, trained in both counselling and aspects of hearing impairment, who would function as part of the multidisciplinary team, liaising with other members as necessary, and whose main purpose would be to work with the family through the diagnostic crisis, aiming to gradually withdraw as the family regained their own power and control. This person should not be an 'adviser', or a 'guider', or a 'hidden manipulator', but a facilitator who can help parents regain their self-respect and self-esteem, and realize the full potential of their child, instead of the present situation where many parents are left with unresolved feelings of anger and grief, and a sense of failure, which may then be passed on to the child.

Each member of the team – for example, the audiologist, teacher of the deaf, speech therapist, etc. – has their own specific role and their own expertise to offer a family with a deaf child. The facilitator could be seen by parents to have a distinct role, separate from other members of the team (yet also a part of the team). This person would be someone to whom parents could release their emotions of anger, hurt, fear, etc., so that these emotions could be skilfully directed away from other personnel who are working with the child. If parents are left with negative emotions towards a particular professional (as was found in several of the interviews for the present study) – whether from real or imagined cause – it is the child, ultimately, who is going to suffer.

Parents who are treated insensitively at the time of diagnosis, or who are given what turn out to be false claims about the achievement potential of their children, are likely to become disillusioned, bitter and resentful. Their self-esteem is likely to drop, and this is likely to have repercussions for their child. It requires a great deal of skill and experience to help parents to separate out the confused emotions that follow a diagnosis of hearing loss. Sometimes a professional's wish to 'make it better' for parents, in order to lessen the impact of the shock of diagnosis, can actually set children up to be failures from the outset. For example, the suggestion that 'if your child learns sign language he or she will never learn to speak' (a claim for which there is no evidence) implies that the child will otherwise grow up to speak normally. By the time that child reaches an age where there is clearly no progress in speech development, and the parents are guided towards a special school that uses signing, the child is already seen as an 'oral failure' in the eyes of the parents. Trying to shield parents from anxiety may, in the long term, make the situation far worse. At the end of the day it is the parents who carry the burden of responsibility and make decisions for their child, until that child is able to do this for him or her self.

The question then arises, who should be the facilitator? Various suggestions have been put forward by different authors for a person trained in counselling in this field. For example, Muller (1978) contended that the traditional role of the speech pathologist and the audiologist should be expanded to include counselling, while Enright (1982) has suggested that the advisory teacher might take on this role. For the reasons stated above, I argue that the facilitator needs to have a distinct and separate role. The personal qualities of the facilitator are more important than the professional background from which he or she has stemmed.

However, a health visitor with additional training would be a strong contender. As discussed on page 127, counselling and interpersonal skills development is embraced within their training (although an additional qualification in counselling would be required). They have a nursing background, and can therefore translate medical terminology from doctors and consultants to the family if the need arises. They are trained in child development and assessment, with particular emphasis on the under-5s, and can therefore discuss and separate out aspects of hearing loss from other aspects of child development when parents have concerns. (In the present study, questions arose about sleeping problems and behavioural difficulties which no one was able to discuss with the parents.) Health visitors are accustomed to being used as resources, passing on information and knowing where to obtain it, and specialist health visitors already exist. A health visitor would also be in a good position to liaise with all health visitor colleagues (whether or not they have deaf children on their care loads), to discuss hearing screening techniques and aim to improve the current situation where some children are passing screening checks when they have profound hearing losses.

At present, as discussed throughout the present study, deaf children with poor communication skills have poor educational achievement and poor employment prospects and, in the current economic climate of high unemployment, their chances of obtaining a good job deteriorate further. Yet Groce (1982), in her study of Martha's Vineyard, has documented that deaf people were equal to hearing people in terms of employment, finance and status. The difference between deaf and hearing people was removed once the barrier to communication was removed: everyone, both deaf and hearing, used sign language. If deaf people can be given sign as their first language, they are far more likely to then develop spoken English as a second language. It therefore makes economic sense to encourage sign language, so that deaf people will be enabled to contribute to society rather than, as at present, often adding an extra (and quite unnecessary) burden on already overstretched services.

Another factor to be considered in economic terms is the demand on the psychological services. The fact that deaf children have a higher incidence of emotional and behavioural difficulties than do hearing children has been discussed throughout the present study, yet it has also been found that these difficulties diminish as the child develops a means of communication. Again it makes economic (as well as moral) sense to encourage sign language, and also to employ a specialist facilitator who can help parents with these difficulties and, it is hoped, prevent long-term problems from arising.

Denmark (1990) has argued that when parents unite together they have power, and that they should be campaigning for improved facilities for their hearing-impaired children; but until parents are given information they are not even aware of the issues for which they should be campaigning.

Professionals are powerful and are in a position of control at a time when parents are at their most vulnerable – during the diagnostic crisis. Professionals need to listen to parents and work with them as part of a team. Barriers of fear and professional biases need to be broken down, and horizons need to be broadened to consider all aspects of a child's life, rather than viewing it from the narrow perspective of a single discipline (that is, in terms of 'audiology', or 'health', or 'education', etc.), so that professionals from all fields are truly working together in the best interests of children and their families.

Part II

9 A brief overview of hearing and deafness

Introduction

This chapter considers some of the audiological and medical aspects relating to hearing and its impairment. It is intended for the professional reader with little prior knowledge or experience of these aspects.

Aspects covered in this chapter include:

- the physiology and mechanism of hearing;
- definitions of hearing loss;
- measurement and testing of hearing;
- some of the causes of conductive and sensorineural deafness;
- hearing aids;
- cochlear implants.

Information is presented in a simplified form, and throughout the chapter the reader is referred to various sources for further information.

The mechanism of hearing

The human ear is a detector capable of recording almost incredibly minute sounds. It acts as an early warning mechanism, and the two ears working together enable the brain to localize the source of a sound.[1]

The ear

The ear is divided into the outer, middle and inner compartments (see

153

Figure 9.1).

The outer ear

The external canal carries sound waves from the pinna (ear flap) to the tympanum (ear drum) which then vibrates. The tympanum separates the outer ear from the middle ear.

The middle ear

The middle ear is about the size of a marble and is filled with air. It is connected to the pharynx (back of the throat) by the Eustachian tube, which allows pressure of air in the middle ear to equalize with outside pressure.

Vibrations of the tympanum are conveyed through the middle ear via three small bones called the ossicles, or ossicle chain. Because of their shapes the bones are called the malleus (hammer), which is attached to the tympanum, the incus (anvil) and the stapes (stirrup), which is attached to

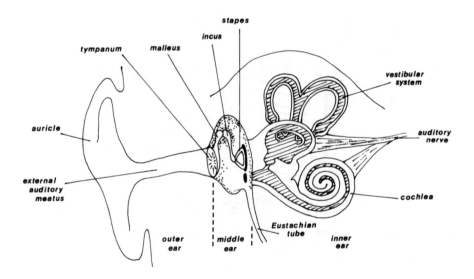

Figure 9.1   Diagram of the ear

the oval window. The oval window sits between the middle ear and the inner ear. The ossicle chain, together with the oval window, transfer energy from air in the middle ear to the liquid environment of the inner ear.

The inner ear

The inner ear has a bony, coiled tube of two-and-a-half turns, called the cochlea, which is divided into three parallel canals. These are called the scala vestibuli, the scala media or cochlear duct, and the scala tympani (see Figure 9.2).

The inner ear is filled with fluid. The scala vestibuli and scala tympani are filled with perilymph, while the cochlear duct is filled with endolymph. Two membranes separate the cochlear duct from the other canals. The upper scala vestibuli is separated by Reissner's membrane, and the lower scala tympani by the basilar membrane.

The round window is set into the wall of the scala tympani. When the stapes (from the middle ear) is pushed into the oval window, a wave is

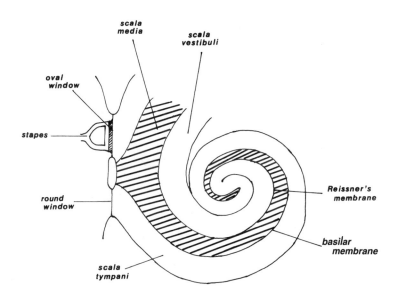

Figure 9.2   Diagram of the inner ear

conducted along the scala vestibuli, through the Reissner's membrane to the cochlear duct. The basilar membrane is depressed and the round window bulges out into the middle ear, where the sound energy is dissipated into the air.

Sound receptors are found in the organ of Corti, which lies on the basilar membrane. It is made up of hair cells (Corti cells), arranged into inner and outer groups, with supporting cells. Each hair cell is anchored on the basilar membrane and has a bundle of hairs projecting upwards. The hair cells make contact at their base with fibres from the auditory nerve (the eighth cranial nerve).

Individual hair cells vary in length and stiffness. The short, stiff ones are more sensitive to high frequencies than the longer, more flexible ones.

When a wave travels along the basilar membrane the hair cells are mechanically stimulated. Bending of the hairs triggers the release of a chemical transmitter, which in turn activates the cochlear fibres.

A sound stimulus contains four properties: pitch, intensity, duration of the stimulus and direction of the sound source.

Central auditory pathways

The auditory pathway leads from the cochlea to the primary auditory cortex which lies deep in the brain, and has several relay stations along the route.[2] The brain has centres which are specialized for analysing individual sounds to work out their direction of origin. It also has higher centres which are able to recognize the source and nature of sounds and the content of speech. The ascending system provides stimulation from one ear to both sides of the brain, while descending fibres from each side of the brain provide inhibition to both cochleas. The relay stations process the incoming nerve impulses, so that recoding and processing of information takes place all the way up through the system (Martin 1986b).

Sound

Sound can be defined in terms of either psychological or physical phenomena. In the psychological sense, sound is an auditory experience – the act of hearing something. In the physical sense, it is a series of disturbances of molecules within an elastic medium (Martin 1986a).

Sound is caused by variation in air pressure within a specified range of frequencies and intensities. Outside this range the sensations produced are described as vibration, flutter, tickle and pain (Bray et al 1989).

Soundwaves

A source of sound, such as a tuning fork, causes the surrounding air molecules to oscillate and spread out in waves of compression (high pressure) alternating with rarefaction (low pressure). The loudness of sound is related to the difference in pressure of the soundwave (the amplitude), while pitch is related to the frequency of the soundwave. A soundwave must have a medium to support it. There can be no soundwaves in a vacuum (Rosenberg 1982).

Elasticity

The medium that supports a soundwave must have elasticity – the molecules must rebound after being displaced. All substances possess enough elasticity to support soundwaves (whether solid, liquid or gas). As a general rule, soundwaves travel more slowly in gases than liquids, and more slowly in liquids than solids, but there are exceptions (for example, soundwaves travel faster in helium and hydrogen). The speed of soundwaves is also affected by temperature (increases in temperature lead to an increase in speed); amplitude (waves of a very high amplitude, for example in the vicinity of an explosion, travel faster); and the shape of the medium (for example, soundwaves will travel more slowly in a tube) (Rosenberg 1982).

Frequency

Frequency refers to the number of waves passing a point in a second, and is measured in cycles per second. Hertz (Hz) is the international unit for the measurement of frequency, where one cycle per second equals 1 Hertz. The greater the frequency, the higher the pitch.

The human ear is capable of perceiving frequencies from as low as 20 Hz to 20 000 Hz, which is nearly ten octaves of pitch range, although most speech is in the range of 500 Hz to 2 000 Hz and is a mixture of these frequencies (Alpiner 1970). A pure tone is a sound of only one frequency, but sounds rarely consist of one pure tone, they are usually complex, comprising a combination of tones of different frequencies.

Intensity

The concept of 'loudness' is subjective and therefore difficult to measure, so the intensity of sound is measured instead.

A single wave carries a particular quantity of energy, and a succession of waves produces a flow of energy. The amount of energy depends on the amplitude and frequency of the vibrations, the density of the medium, and the speed (velocity) of the soundwaves. A soundwave travelling away from its source can be imagined as an expanding spherical surface. The total energy of the wave remains unchanged, but the intensity decreases with distance because the energy becomes more thinly spread (Rosenberg 1982).

The term 'sound pressure' is often used interchangeably with the term 'intensity'. It is measured in decibels (dB or db) after Alexander Graham Bell, the inventor of the telephone (Wright 1987).

Decibels   A decibel is defined as: 'A unit used to express the ratio of two powers, usually electric or acoustic powers, equal to one-tenth the common logarithm of the ratio of the powers. One decibel is equal approximately to the smallest difference in acoustic power that the human ear can detect', while: 'bel is the common logarithm of the ratio of two powers, usually electric or acoustic powers. An increase of one bel in intensity approximately doubles the loudness of most sounds' (*Dorland's Illustrated Medical Dictionary* 1985). Because of this, the bel turns out to be too large a unit to be convenient for measurement, therefore the numbers are multiplied by ten to obtain smaller units one-tenth of the size, hence the decibel (Pickles 1987).

The range of intensities that the human ear can detect is extremely wide. The loudest sound we can hear without damaging our ears has a level about 120 dB above the faintest sound we can detect. This corresponds to a ratio of powers of 1 000 000 000 000:1 (Moore 1982; see Figure 9.3).

Although the decibel scale expresses relative energy, it is used to describe absolute values by using an agreed reference standard.[3] References are given for intensity and pressure. These are related, and represent the typical hearing threshold in man at the frequency where hearing is most sensitive. When pressure readings are used to measure sound we speak of the sound pressure level (SPL) in dB.

The threshold of hearing (that is, the quietest sound that a person can detect) is 0 dB (SPL) and a jet engine is 120 dB (SPL) (see Figure 9.3).

Defining hearing loss

The term 'hearing impairment' is defined as: 'loss of hearing that is severe enough to produce disorders of communication requiring remedial or educational treatment' (Rodda and Grove 1987, p.1). Although this is a continuum, for practical purposes hearing loss is divided into two groups – 'deaf' and 'hard of hearing', and different educational methods are required for the two groups.

As well as the degree of impairment, the age of onset is also a crucial factor in defining hearing loss. Children who are born deaf, or lose their hearing

NOISE	DECIBELS	RELATIVE ENERGY	EXAMPLE
DEAFENING	120	1 000 000 000 000	Jet Engine (500 Feet)
	110	100 000 000 000	Pop Group Motor Horn (5 Feet)
	100	10 000 000 000	
VERY LOUD	90	1 000 000 000	Workshop
	80	100 000 000	Radio – Full Volume
LOUD	70	10 000 000	
	60	1 000 000	Normal Conversation
MODERATE	50	100 000	Quiet Office
	40	10 000	Public Library
FAINT	30	1 000	Whisper
	20	100	Quiet Church
VERY FAINT	10	10	
	0	1	Threshold of Hearing

(Reproduced by kind permission of Mr Harry Kernahan, University of Hertfordshire)

Figure 9.3   Typical noises and their rating

before they acquire language, have a much greater problem than those who become deaf after they have developed spoken language.

Hearing loss is divided into four categories:

- slightly hearing-impaired – children whose average hearing loss, regardless of age of onset, does not exceed 40 dB;
- moderately hearing-impaired – children whose average hearing loss, regardless of age of onset, is from 41 dB to 70 dB;

- severely hearing-impaired – children whose average hearing loss is from 71 dB to 95 dB, and those with a greater loss who acquired their hearing impairment after the age of 18 months;
- profoundly hearing-impaired – children who were born with, or acquired before the age of 18 months, an average loss of 96 dB or greater.[4]

Incidence and prevalence

The incidence of a disease is the number of cases which come into being during a specified time period, and the incidence rate is this number per specified unit of population. In practice it is not usually possible to measure incidence directly, as the exact time of onset of the disease is usually unknown (MacMahon and Pugh 1970).

Prevalence is the total number of cases present, and the prevalence rate is defined as the existing number of cases of an illness or disorder in a specified time period (Shewan et al 1987). Prevalence estimates for congenital deafness vary, partly because definitions and reporting of hearing loss are not standardized (Sancho et al 1988); and the loss may be transient or permanent, and may extend over all frequencies or may only affect certain ranges (Peckham 1986).

Estimates for prelingual deafness in children appear to be fairly consistent, varying between 0.8 per 1 000 live births (Newton 1985) and 1.6 per 1 000 live births (DHSS 1977). Approximately 1 child per 1 000 is profoundly deaf (Bellman 1987).

The distribution of deaf adults in the population is less clear-cut. A Medical Research Council national study suggests that up to 10 per cent of the adult population in the UK (or 4.2 million people) have a severe hearing disability, and as many as 10 million people suffer some degree of loss (Davis 1983). Approximately 2 million people use hearing aids (Martin and Grover 1986).

The Education Act 1981 altered the way that statistics are collected for educational provision for children with special needs. Since 1983 special education is no longer categorized by handicap (DES 1985), and personal social services statistics no longer categorize the deaf and hard of hearing separately.

Hearing testing and measurement

The word 'audiometry' is derived from the Latin *audire*, to hear, and the Greek *metrios*, to measure, but today the word is not just confined to the measurement of hearing, it also produces a sophisticated tool for diagnosis (West 1985).

Hearing can be tested in a number of different ways. Some tests are subjective, requiring the cooperation of the person being tested, but increasingly more objective tests are coming into being. Hearing can be tested at any age if a hearing loss is suspected.

Hearing screening

Virtually all children in the UK are screened for hearing between 7 and 9 months of age, but results have proven disappointing (Bellman 1987). For example, Martin et al (1981) highlighted that only 55 per cent of children with a loss of 50 dB or greater were identified by 3 years of age, while Newton (1985) found in Manchester that the average age at identification of presumed congenital hearing loss was 23.3 months. Although in some districts the results are said to be satisfactory, according to Bellman (1987) these figures would be typical of the results in many areas of the UK. The two main problems encountered are the initial passing of screening checks of many children with hearing loss, and the low attendance rate for screening in many districts.

In the present study, when 142 parents of not-yet-tested children were asked what they thought about routine hearing testing, the vast majority gave a positive response (97 percent).[5] Only one parent considered routine hearing testing to be not very useful. Rather than offering a range of responses, the question was open-ended. The responses obtained were remarkably similar and were divided into three groups: 'essential', 'very important' and 'necessary' as one (36 per cent); 'valuable', 'useful' and 'good idea' as a second (61 per cent), and 'not very useful' as a third (0.7 per cent) (see Figure 9.4). Three respondents did not reply.

This result linked favourably with the responses of 49 health visitors in the same geographical area, on the numbers of infants receiving hearing tests; 88 per cent of parents attended for hearing tests with their infants, and approximately 98 per cent of infants received a hearing test within the first year of life (home visits accounted for the 10 per cent discrepancy). Only one health visitor answered that quite a lot of his or her clients did not receive a test in the first year of life. (This could be due to a variety of factors; one being a highly mobile client population where there was difficulty keeping track of families) (see Figure 9.4).

But are parents right to be so positive about routine hearing screening? The Hall Report (Hall 1989) found that standard tests were failing to pick up many cases of inherited deafness, and that, generally, deafness was not picked up until the child was 3 years old, when parents noticed that speech was affected.

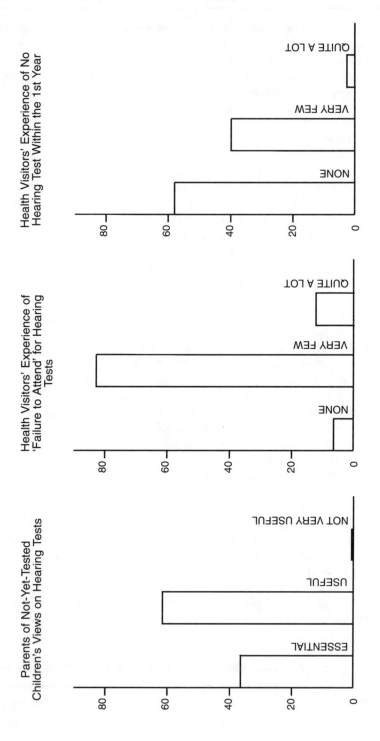

Figure 9.4 Comparison of parents' views of hearing testing with health visitors' experience of attendance for hearing tests and failure to receive a hearing test in the first year

The Hall Report states: 'when inadequately performed the distraction screening test is not merely valueless but is positively harmful and may persuade parents that worries are unfounded' (p.63). Confirmation of this can be found in the following examples taken from interviews by the author with parents of hearing-impaired children:

> She passed the 8-month check. She didn't turn to some sounds but the lady at the front said she thought she responded with her eyes. I wanted everything to be alright. I wasn't worried so I was happy about it.

> I wondered if he was deaf when he failed his first hearing test. They said he passed. He didn't. He failed on his left ear. They classed it as a pass but I wasn't very happy then and they said leave it until he's older, and as he was getting older I realized that there were things that were wrong, especially when he started to regress and lose words that he'd already gained.

> He failed a hearing test at 6 weeks. We were told not to worry, to come back at 8 months. He failed at 8 months and we were told to come back in another month. He was nearly a year before he was diagnosed profoundly deaf.

> I knew she was deaf from when she was 11 weeks. I told the GP – we were seen at the hospital the next day. She came into the hospital for ten days. They didn't check her hearing. They tested her for cystic fibrosis. At the 7-month check she failed. The health visitor referred her straightaway. She didn't re-test her because she had so clearly failed. The appointment took a long time – months. We were back and forth to the doctor's so many times. Then we were referred to [the hospital] but never received the appointment. Eventually I went back to the GP and we were referred to [another hospital]. She was profoundly deaf. She literally hadn't heard. She was 2½ years.

According to the Hall Report, parents' concerns must be taken seriously, and no parent who is worried about any aspect of their child's development should be denied access to the appropriate professional for expert assessment. Yet sometimes, as in the following example, parents have great difficulty in gaining access to expert opinion:

> At around 9–10 months she had repeated ear infections. I asked for a referral but was just given a prescription for antibiotics all over the winter. Eventually we had a private referral. She was found to have glue ear and had grommets put in two weeks later. It was then that I began to realize she wasn't hearing and I asked for another referral. That's when we found she had a permanent [sensorineural] loss. The doctor only referred because I kept on asking – and said there wasn't any need. It would have been better if that hadn't been said.

McCormick et al (1984) have shown that, with proper training of health visitors in hearing screening procedures, the use of supplementary health education techniques, and open access clinics, in most cases the time lapse before the identification of congenitally deafened babies may be substantially reduced to within the first year of life.

Neonatal screening

Research has been carried out since the 1950s to identify behaviour responses which might be suitable for screening neonates for deafness (Wharrad 1988), and advances in electrophysiological techniques and computer hardware and software have led to the development of various devices for hearing screening in early infancy (Sancho et al 1988).[6]

Behavioural responses to sound include respiration and heart rate, reflexes (for example, the eye blink), sucking responses, and body and head movements. Various devices have been, and are being, developed in an attempt to measure hearing accurately from these behavioural responses. At present two automatic screening devices are being evaluated: the Crib-O-Gram (COG), and the Auditory Response Cradle (ARC).

Two other methods currently being researched are the Multi-channel Infant Reflex Audiometry (MIRA) method, which simultaneously monitors sucking, breathing and eye movement responses to sound, and the Behavioural Screening Device (BSD), which has been designed to investigate various responses to sound in pre-term and full-term babies (Wharrad 1988).

Interest has also focused on auditory brainstem-evoked responses (ABR). For example, the Body Spek 2000 hearing screening unit is designed to measure and record responses electronically through electrodes fixed to a baby's skin – the post-auricular myogenic (PAM) response. The responses are based on involuntary reflex, so no active response is required from the baby. A series of clicks are transmitted on a selected level of intensity, and the responses are displayed digitally on a screen (Bigglestone 1986). However, this method is affected by the age of the infant being tested. Neonates below 36 weeks gestational age have immature brainstem responses and may fail on initial ABR testing. For this reason Alberti (1986) advocates deferring testing until 3 months or so, in order to avoid high numbers of false positives.

This test is time-consuming and requires experienced personnel as well as specialized equipment. Because of the high cost it is difficult to justify screening the whole neonatal population, although it is justifiable to screen those in the high-risk groups (Bellman 1987).

According to Wharrad (1988), until more information is available it is impossible to predict which will prove the most effective method overall. She considers that, of the three methods currently being evaluated, behavioural methods are most likely to fulfil the requirement.

Subjective hearing tests

The behavioural response to sound matures with the child's development in the same way as other skills, so different kinds of tests are used depending on the maturational level of the child (Bellman 1987). Prior to approximately 7 months of age the child is unable to localize sound accurately, so although subjective tests may give an indication of hearing loss, it is not an accurate measure.

According to McCormick (1988b), testing children below 3 years of age by behavioural methods poses many problems which can be overcome by the skilled tester. Paediatric audiologists require training to develop skills in child handling, timing and clinical decision-making.

There are several subjective tests available for children. The distraction test is used for infants from 6 to18 months. It is based on the principle that a baby turns its head to the source of a sound. Two testers are required, and the baby must be able to sit erect and turn the head in response to sounds.

By the time the child reaches 18 months they should be able to understand simple verbal instructions, and so the cooperative test is used. Play is used in a giving game – for example, 'give this to teddy'. However, children between 18 and 30 months are the most difficult group to test, as this is a negative period, and can prove a challenge to the testers (McCormick 1988a).

For children with mental ages of $2^1/2$ years and above, the performance test is used. The child waits for a sound then responds in a play activity, such as placing a peg on a board. This can be a useful test for children with language difficulties as no verbal instructions are used.

A further behavioural technique is visual reinforcement audiometry (VRA), which is generally usable with children between 6–9 months through to 3 years. It is widely used in the USA, Australia and New Zealand, but is, as yet, little used in the UK (Bamford 1988). The child and parents are left alone in the testing room with some toys on a table. (Parents are given instructions before the tester leaves the room.) Sounds are presented from a loudspeaker, and the visual reinforcer (such as a toy animal with eyes that light up) is presented with the sound.

The most widely used hearing test is pure-tone audiometry, and the pure-tone audiometer tests hearing sensitivity at a number of different frequencies (Martin 1986a). Pure tones (tones with a single frequency of vibration) are presented via headphones (air conduction) or via a bone vibrator (bone conduction), and the threshold of hearing is measured.

According to Wood (1988) the definition of auditory threshold is, to some extent, an arbitrary one. There will be an intensity at and above which the patient responds on 100 per cent of the presentations, and a lower intensity at which the patient will fail to respond on 100 per cent of the presentations. In between these two intensities is a region where the threshold lies. Certain variables can affect the threshold, such as the attention, motivation and concentration ability of the patient, background noise, instructions to the patient, etc.

Although pure-tone audiometry is helpful, none of us hears pure tones in real life, so speech audiometry may be used as an alternative.

In the same way that pure-tone audiometry measures the auditory threshold, speech audiometry measures the speech-detection threshold – that is, the level at which a listener can just detect the presence of an on-going speech signal and identify it as speech (Martin 1981). To use speech audiometry, patients must know and understand the words used for the test. Depending on the type of test, the responses must by obtained by an oral response, a written reply, or by identifying a picture or object. For this reason full-speech audiometry is not suitable for the very young child (under 3 years of age), and so a simplified form is used, where the child discriminates between simple, familiar instructions or requests. However, if the speech and language development is affected by the severity of the hearing loss it may not be possible to undertake this test (McCormick 1988a).

Objective hearing tests

Two kinds of objective testing are currently available. These are acoustic admittance measurements, which are used to determine middle ear functioning, and electric response audiometry, to investigate sensorineural loss.

Acoustic admittance measurement   The middle ear transfers energy from air into the fluid medium of the inner ear. If the tympanic membrane is not working properly it may impede the passage of sound to the cochlea, or it may admit more energy than normal. The acoustic admittance provides a measure of the efficiency of the middle ear in receiving and relaying the sound energy that enters the ear canal (see Brooks 1988 for further information).

The majority of admittance procedures involve a probe which contains a small transducer that can produce a low-frequency tone. The probe is placed either in the canal or against the entrance so that a seal is obtained. A low-frequency tone is produced in the canal. If the tympanic membrane is normal, and is connected to a normally-operating middle ear, most of the sound energy will be absorbed and passed on to the cochlea. Only a small amount will be reflected back into the ear canal. If the middle ear is not working normally (for example, with glue ear) then most of the energy will be reflected back into the ear canal. The sound pressure level can be measured by a microphone set into the probe.

Electric response audiometry All the levels of the sensorineural part of the auditory system respond electrically when stimulated. When electrodes are applied to the surface of the skin at appropriate sites it is possible to detect and separately identify activity in the cochlea, the auditory nerve and the cerebral cortex (Rosenberg 1982). Changes are detected and recorded on paper tracings by means of an electroencephalogram (EEG) and analysed by computer.[7]

The electrical response is known by a number of different names, but is most commonly called the 'auditory evoked potential'. Auditory evoked potentials can be recorded from the ear, brainstem and cortex of the auditory pathway, and responses are divided into those arising from the cochlea and auditory nerve, electrocochleography (ECochG), and those recorded from the brainstem pathways, the auditory brainstem response (ABR) (Mason 1988).

ECochG is an invasive technique which requires a general anaesthetic and sterile procedures. An electrode is placed through the tympanic membrane to the cochlea, and the nerve action recorded. An alternative method is available which involves placing an electrode in the ear canal close to the tympanic membrane. Both techniques require either general anaesthetic or sedation for a young child.

Auditory brainstem-evoked responses require a still child, so the child may require sedation for the technique. According to Mason (1988), children are usually referred for electric response audiometry tests because conventional tests have failed to provide reliable or adequate results, and the ABR is now an established tool for the assessment of hearing loss in children.

Hearing impairment

> Any abnormal condition or disease process which interferes with the conduction of sound to the inner ear, with the transduction of nerve impulses in the cochlea, or with their transmission to the appropriate levels of the nervous system, can cause an impairment in hearing. (Best and Taylor 1966, p.416)

Hearing impairment can be divided into conductive impairment, caused by interference with the passage of sound waves through the outer and middle ear, and sensorineural impairment, caused by damage to the cochlea mechanism and/or to the auditory nerve. It is possible to have mixed deafness, with both conductive and sensorineural loss in the same ear, and also to have non-organic deafness (Adams 1987a).

Conductive deafness is often fully treatable, either medically or with hearing aids, whereas sensorineural deafness is usually medically irreversible and is only partly helped by amplification with hearing aids

(Quigley and Paul 1984).

Conductive deafness mainly tends to affect low notes, which in speech terms means the vowels, whereas sensorineural deafness is particularly liable to affect high notes which define some consonants, although it may affect all tones equally.

Hearing loss associated with injury to the hair cells may be accompanied by 'recruitment', where there is a more rapid growth of loudness than normal (that is, a person may suddenly hear a loud sound with no prior build-up towards it). This can sometimes cause problems for someone wearing hearing aids that are adjusted for everyday speech, as some sounds may be uncomfortably loud (West 1985).

There can be temporary forms of deafness in both conductive and sensorineural impairment. For example, in conductive impairment the drum membrane can become strongly retracted by a negative pressure in the middle ear, as can be caused when an aircraft is descending, so that air is absorbed and the middle ear rapidly fills with fluid (Best and Taylor 1966). This condition reverses once the the pressure equalizes and the fluid is absorbed.

Temporary sensorineural impairment can occur from continuous exposure to sound (Rosenberg 1982). Continuous exposure to sound of intensity 75–85 dB causes a temporary impairment known as 'auditory fatigue'. There is an increase in the threshold of hearing (that is, the quietest sound that can be detected), referred to as a 'temporary threshold shift'. When a person enters a noisy place and stays there, that person's hearing threshold starts to rise and continues rising for several hours until it reaches a plateau level (the level will depend on the intensity of the noise). When the person leaves the noisy environment the threshold begins to fall, but it may take 24 hours or so to return to 'normal'. A car travelling at speed can be as loud as 80 dB or more, and a few hours is sufficient to cause a substantial and long-lasting threshold shift. The noise does not have to be continuous – intermittent sounds of minutes or even seconds duration have a cumulative effect.

Permanent damage

Both of the above temporary conditions are normally reversible, but if there is continuous or intense exposure to very loud noise, then the change can become permanent. Routine exposure to noise of 90 dB or more causes irreversible damage to hearing (Rosenberg 1982).

Soundwaves of high intensity can destroy the hair cells in the cochlea, and there has been much concern about the high levels of sound endured from discos, hi-fis and personal stereos for several years.

In a recent report (NDCS 1990) the danger of personal stereos was further highlighted. Seven personal stereo systems were tested. With one exception, all peak levels were greater than 90 dB. Some peaks exceeded 100 dB. Because decibels are a logarithmic scale of sound measurement, a sound of 100 dB has ten times as much energy as one of 90 dB (to put it in context, 100 dB can be compared to a pneumatic road drill, see also Figure 9.3). If a sound source is removed and a person suffers temporary ringing in the ears, 'then it is almost certain that they have already suffered some measure of damage to their hearing, though this may not be immediately apparent. Further exposure to loud sounds will increase the damage done' (NDCS 1990, p.4).

Causes of deafness

Deafness can occur at any age.[8] Many different factors can affect hearing, including hereditary factors, congenital abnormalities, blockages, toxic conditions (from drugs or infection), trauma, localized disease, tumours, radiation treatment and systemic diseases (West 1985).

Genetics and deafness

Explained simply, autosomes are the 22 pairs of chromosomes which are not the sex chromosomes (that is, X and Y), while genes are units of hereditary information present on the chromosomes. Autosomes pair according to their shape, so every gene occurs twice in every cell of the body. In every pregnancy one of the genes for hearing will be passed to the child from each parent.[9]

Autosomal recessive deafness

This is the commonest form of inherited deafness. In its simplest form the gene for hearing exists in both a normal and abnormal form in both parents. The parents will have normal hearing because of the normal gene. There is a 25 per cent chance that any child will inherit two abnormal genes and so be deaf. There is a 50 per cent chance that they will inherit one abnormal gene and so become a carrier, able to pass the condition on should they marry someone who is also a carrier. This condition is not usually passed from a deaf parent to child unless both deaf parents happen to be carriers.

Autosomal dominant deafness

With this condition a single abnormal gene causes deafness, even when a normal gene is also present. The deafness may vary from mild to profound, and be bilateral or unilateral. There is a 50 per cent chance of each child receiving the abnormal gene.

X-linked deafness

This form of deafness occurs in males, having been passed on by unaffected females. It is extremely rare. There are also rare X-linked syndromes which include deafness.

Inherited deafness can be present at birth or may appear later in childhood, and can cause either conductive or sensorineural loss. A wide range of syndromes which can be autosomal recessive, autosomal dominant or X-linked can cause varying degrees of deafness from birth, including a rare group where hearing appears to be normal at birth with a gradual onset of deafness.

Certain associated diseases may give rise to conductive deafness – for example, cystic fibrosis, where thick mucus blocks the Eustachian tube and middle ear, and osteogenesis imperfecta (brittle bone disease), although not all children with this disease have conductive deafness.

Some causes of conductive hearing loss

Conductive deafness can be caused by abnormality of the middle or outer ear (for example, with Down's syndrome); inflammation or infection of the middle ear (otitis media); trauma (whether accidental, non-accidental or surgical); a foreign body, or wax in the external canal. A foreign body must completely block the canal to cause deafness.

Otitis media

This is the most common cause of conductive deafness in childhood, and there are three major forms: acute, secretory and chronic.

With acute otitis media there is an acute illness with high temperature, severe ear pain, and often a discharge from the ear. There is increasing deafness and pain because the middle ear fills with fluid under pressure.

Secretory otitis media is 'unarguably the single most common cause of deafness in childhood, occurring in children of all ages' (Gibbin 1988, p.51). With this condition (often called 'glue ear') the middle ear fills with fluid, which in time becomes thick and sticky like glue.

With chronic otitis media the middle ear cavity continues to discharge fluid through a perforation. There is often infection present, and slow progressive damage occurs to the tympanum and ossicles. Recently links have been made between passive smoking and middle ear effusion (Strachan et al 1989).

Some causes of sensorineural deafness

As with conductive loss, sensorineural deafness may result from congenital or acquired disorders, including maternal infections passed to the foetus across the placenta (for example, rubella, or cytomegalovirus, etc.); ototoxic drugs; metabolic disorders, and neoplastic disorders.

Rubella

Rubella is the most common identifiable cause of congenital sensorineural deafness in children (Martin 1982). Deafness occurs in about one-third of rubella children, and Hardy (1973) has shown that infection with the virus at any stage in pregnancy can cause deafness, not just if infection occurs in the first trimester, which is a common mistaken belief.

A rubella vaccine has been available since 1970 for girls aged 10–14, and women of childbearing age. However, uptake of the vaccine was disappointing, even after a concerted effort by the DHSS in 1983 to increase vaccination (CDR 87/03). In 1988 a new vaccine, measles, mumps and rubella (MMR), was introduced, and is now offered to all children (boys and girls) in infancy, so that the vaccination of school girls will eventually be phased out.

Cytomegalovirus

Congenital cytomegalovirus (CMV) is the most common congenital infection in the UK, affecting 3–4 infants per 1 000 births (Peckham et al 1983). Most infants who are affected do not show any symptoms, and often the virus is unrecognized. Nevertheless, many unexplained cases of senso-rineural deafness may be due to this infection, and could account for approximately 12 per cent of all children with sensorineural loss (Peckham et al 1987).

Perinatal disorders

There are three major causes of sensorineural deafness in the perinatal period: hypoxia (insufficient oxygen), disorders associated with raised bilirubin levels (jaundice), and problems associated with prematurity and low birth weight (Adams 1987a).

Pre-term delivery (before the 37th week of pregnancy) and low birth weight (weighing less than 2 500 g) are very closely linked, and infants in these groups have a higher incidence of hearing loss than normal (Minoli and Moro 1985), although the causes are varied. Pre-term babies are more likely to suffer episodes of hypoxia, and are generally at risk because of their immaturity. They are very prone to life-threatening infections, and may well be given antibiotics which are potentially harmful to the auditory system (ototoxic). It has also been suggested by Taylor (1979) that the high, prolonged level of incubator noise may be a factor, although this remains theoretical at present.

Acquired disorders

Meningitis is the most frequent cause of acquired sensorineural deafness in childhood, and about 10 per cent of children with meningitis will develop some degree of hearing loss (Martin 1982). In some children with bacterial meningitis the initial loss will recover in six months (Munoz et al 1983).

Certain drugs may be ototoxic. These include a particular group of antibiotics (which includes Neomycin, Erythromycin, Streptomycin, etc.), and cytotoxic drugs which are used in the treatment of childhood cancers (Adams 1987a).

Other causes include certain rare diseases of the immune system, tumours, cancers such as leukaemia, and trauma. A blow on the head that is severe enough to render a child unconscious can damage the cochlea.

Non-organic deafness

Non-organic deafness can occur in three forms: hysterical deafness, malingering, or where organic disease is present in a mild form (Adams 1987a). Hysterical deafness is very uncommon in children under 5 years, and is often stress-related. There may be psychological problems, such as aggressive or withdrawn behaviour. With malingering there is intention on the part of the child to deceive. It is rare in children, because most cannot keep up the pretence for long. Children with non-organic deafness occasionally appear to be much deafer than can be explained by the pathology.

All three groups present difficult management problems, and may need referral to a child psychologist or psychiatrist.

Hearing aids

'A hearing aid is a device which processes sound in such a way as to make the information it conveys more accessible to the user' (Evans 1988, p.265). Hearing aids come in various shapes and sizes, some worn on the body, some behind the ear, and others within the bowl of the ear or within the ear canal. Hearing aids can also be built into or attached to spectacle frames (Martin and Grover 1986).

All hearing aids are amplifiers – they make sound louder – and all aids have a similar set of parts: a microphone, amplifier with volume control, earphone and battery. There are differences in the range of tones covered and amount of amplification.

Two types of hearing aids are currently available for children: personal hearing aids, and hearing aid systems (Tucker and Nolan 1984).

According to Martin (1979), although a wide range of aids is available and can provide amplification for losses ranging from very small to profound, tests to determine optimum amplification take considerable time. Without sufficient time the fitting of hearing aids basically amounts to guesswork, and ultimately only the patient can judge if the aid meets his or her needs. However, as Adams (1987b) pointed out, young children cannot say which aid, or settings on the aid, they prefer, so aftercare is of prime importance, and must be an integral part of the total hearing aid service.

There has been some controversy over the relative merits of behind-the-ear aids and body-worn aids (Adams 1987b). Behind-the-ear aids give a more natural social environment because sound is received at ear level, they are free from the rubbing of clothes, give improved localization of sound, and are cosmetically more acceptable; however, they are more easily removed and thrown away by young children (although children with a body-worn aid can pull the cord and displace the receiver from the ear).

Nolan (1983) has argued that the most important difficulty with all types of powerful hearing aid is acoustic feedback. This is most likely to occur when the microphone of the aid is close to the receiver or earmould; body-worn aids are less susceptible to this problem as they are worn on the chest. Well-fitting earmoulds are essential if behind-the-ear aids are used, and hearing aids must be checked daily by parents or teachers.

Phonic Ear

The Phonic Ear (mentioned on page 72) is a computerized, wireless hearing aid system which was developed in the USA and has been available in the UK since the mid-1970s. The teacher wears a transmitter, speaks into a microphone, and the sound is picked up by the pupil. According to Bates and Holsgrove (1979), the Phonic Ear system comprises three main parts:

A microphone/transmitter, usually worn by the teacher, broadcasts sounds picked up by the microphone on a particular wavelength denoted by coloured dots on the case. These signals are received by the pupils' body-worn units when the appropriate 'receiver module' (i.e. the one whose colour code corresponds to that of the transmitter) is fitted. The pupils' unit can also function as normal hearing aids. The third item of equipment is the charger unit in which the batteries in the transmitters and receivers are re-charged. (pp.165–6)

Earmoulds

An earmould is the part of a hearing aid system which connects the hearing aid to the ear. It is made from an impression taken of the ear (similar to the way that dentures are made). According to Nolan (1988), an earmould must be comfortable to wear, easy to fit and remove, have a good cosmetic appearance, be easy to clean, and provide a good fit in the ear canal. Should any of these factors not be satisfied the hearing aid is likely to be ineffective. For example, if the earmould is not a good fit it can cause discomfort, so the child may continually remove it, or it may cause acoustic feedback (continuous whistling noise). Earmoulds need to be changed quite regularly, particularly in a young child (whose ears grow very rapidly). An earmould may only last two to three months.[10]

Cochlear implants

According to Martin (1986a), the cochlear implant was the first major step in surgical implantation of hearing aids for patients with profound sensorineural hearing losses who are unable to use conventional amplification. He explains:

> The internal receiver, which is implanted under the skin behind the pinna, consists of wire electrodes and a tiny coil. One (active) electrode is placed in the scala tympani and the other (ground) electrode outside the bony labyrinth. A small microphone, worn outside the body (under the skin, close to the ear) feeds electrical impulses to a small processor, which amplifiers and filters the signal. From the processor the signal goes to a transmitter, which converts it to magnetic impulses that are sent to the two electrodes. An electrical signal is induced from the magnetic field in the cochlea and flows on to stimulate the auditory nerve. (pp.404–5)

Archbold (1992) has argued that cochlear implants can no longer be regarded as research, they are now a clinical provision. Children were first implanted in 1985, and by January 1992 over 600 children worldwide had received the device, although the approach in the UK was more cautious. Although controversy still surrounds the area, a growing awareness of the benefits of the procedure is leading to a demand for wider availability, and in 1989 a specialist cochlear implant programme for children was set up in Nottingham (where the first two children implanted in the UK came from). At present implants are not suitable for all deaf children, and agreed guidelines and criteria are used to decide whether or not to include a child on the programme.

The subject of cochlear implantation has generated a lot of press interest, but, according to Freeland (1989), some media articles have raised false hopes in some people. Results of implantation appear to be enormously variable, and a device capable of reproducing speech is still a long way off. However, as he pointed out, increased awareness of the problems of the deaf can only be to the benefit of the hearing-impaired population, and press attention does help to generate vitally-needed research funds.

Notes

1 For detailed information see Bray et al (1989); Pickles (1987), and West (1985).
2 See Bray et al (1989) and Martin (1986b) for a detailed description of the central auditory pathways.
3 For a more detailed explanation of the decibel and decibel scale see Rosenberg (1982) and Pickles (1987).
4 From ISO (1981).
5 'Not-yet-tested' refers to infants prior to their initial hearing screening test.
6 For further information on neonatal screening see Sancho et al (1988) and Wharrad (1988).
7 For further details see Mason (1988) and Hyde (1987).
8 See West (1985) and Adams (1987a) for causes of conductive and sensorineural loss.
9 See Fraser (1987) and Gibbin (1988) for further information on the genetics of deafness.
10 For further details on hearing aids, the reader is referred to Corcoran (1987) and Evans (1988), and to Nolan (1988) for information regarding earmoulds.

Appendix

Both quantitative and qualitative data were collected for this research. The area chosen for study contained a school for the deaf and two partial-hearing units, one junior mixed infants and one secondary unit.

Quantitative data was collected by means of sample surveys which were administered to:

- Members of the general public (GP – drawn from the electoral register and sent postal questionnaires).
- First-year school children from two comprehensive schools. The schools were chosen because both were involved with integration programmes for children with hearing impairment. One contained a partial-hearing unit, and the second accepted a small group of profoundly deaf children (who used sign language) for partial integration into mainstream classrooms. One class in each school acted as a control group. The classes are identified as follows:

  - Partial Hearing Experience (PHE)
  - Partial Hearing Control (PC)
  - Signing Experience (SE)
  - Signing Control (SC)

  These pupils were tested at the beginning and the end of the school year, hence 'Test 1' and 'Test 2' on the figures in the text.
- Teachers of the deaf (TD – drawn from the school for the deaf, a school for partial-hearing children, and from partial-hearing units in the area).
- Health visitors (drawn from three health authority districts within the county).
- Parents of not-yet-tested children (P-NYT). This sample was collected

via the health visitors who participated in the study. Forms were sent to be filled in by parents whose infant was due to attend for a hearing check (hence the term 'not-yet-tested'). Five forms were sent to each health visitor. As every infant in the UK is offered a hearing check, it was intended that this method would ensure a reasonably representative sample of parents.

Qualitative data was collected by means of interviews and discussion with informed personnel. Parents of deaf and partial-hearing children were interviewed using a focused, in-depth, semi-structured interview format. The children ranged in age from 5 months to the late 30 months.

Other interviews were conducted with a range of people, including: general practitioners, county medical officers, audiologists, paediatricians, educational psychologists, speech therapists, nursing staff, lecturers and researchers in deaf education (both deaf and hearing), house parents for deaf children (both deaf and hearing), a restaurant owner with profoundly deaf customers, and others, both deaf and hearing, with knowledge or experience relating to deafness.

Information gathered from discussion and interviews has been used where appropriate to illustrate and highlight particular discussion points throughout the book.

References

ACREDOLO L. & GOODWYN S. (1988) 'Symbolic gesturing in normal infants'. *Child Development,* Vol. 59, No. 2, pp.450–66.

ADAMS D.A. (1987a) 'The causes of deafness', Ch.4, pp.35–53. In Evans (1987).

ADAMS D.A. (1987b) 'Management of the hearing impaired child', Ch.9. In Evans (1987).

ALBERTI P.W. (1986) 'An evaluation of hearing screening in high risk infants using BERA'. *Audiology in Practice,* Vol. 11, No. 4, pp.3–4.

ALESSANDRI S.M. & WOZNIAK R.H. (1987) 'The child's awareness of parental beliefs concerning the child: a developmental study'. *Child Development,* Vol. 58, No. 2, pp.316–23.

ALESSANDRI S.M. & WOZNIAK R.H. (1989) 'Continuity and change in intrafamilial agreement in beliefs concerning the adolescent: a follow-up study'. *Child Development,* Vol. 60, No. 2, pp.335–9.

ALPINER J.G. (1970) *Speech and Hearing Disorders in Children.* New York: Houghton Mifflin.

ALTSCHULER K.Z. (1974) 'The social and psychological development of the deaf child: problems and their treatment and prevention'. *American Annuals of the Deaf,* Vol. 119, pp.365–76.

APPEL R. & MUYSKEN P. (1988) *Language Contact and Bilingualism.* Edward Arnold. (1st Published 1987.)

ARCHBOLD S. (1992) 'The development of a paediatric cochlear implant programme – a case study'. *Journal of the British Association of Teachers of the Deaf,* Vol. 16, No. 1, pp.17–26.

ARGYLE M. (1976) *The Psychology of Interpersonal Behaviour.* Harmondsworth: Penguin. (1st published 1967.)

ARNBERG L. (1987) *Raising Children Bilingually: The Pre-School Years.* Clevedon, PA: Multilingual Matters.

ARNOLD P. (1982) 'Oralism and the deaf child's brain: a reply to Dr Conrad'. *International Journal of Paediatric Otorhinolaryngology,* Vol. 4, pp.275–86.

ASHER S.R., ODEN S.L. & GOTTMAN J.M. (1977) 'Children's friendships in school settings'. In L.G. Katz (ed.) *Current Topics in Early Childhood Education (Vol. 1).* Norwood, NJ: Ablex.

ASHER S.R. & RENSHAW P.D. (1981) 'Children without friends: social knowledge and social-skills training', pp.272–96. In S.R. Asher and J.M. Gottman (eds) *The Development of Children's Friendships*. Cambridge University Press.

AUDIOLOGY CONFERENCE (1983) *Proceedings of the IV British Conference on Audiology, 4–7 September 1983, University College, London*. London: The British Society of Audiology.

BAKEMAN R. & BROWN J.V. (1980) 'Early interaction: consequences for social and mental development at three years.' *Child Development*. . . Vol. 51, No. 2, pp.437–47.

BAKER I., HUGHES J., STREET E. & SWEETNAM P. (1983) 'Behaviour problems in children followed from 5 to 8¹/₂–9 years of age and their relation to educational attainment'. *Child: Care, Health and Development*, Vol. 9, pp.339–48.

BAKER R. & BREARLEY J. (1989) 'English as a second language for deaf children – what can we learn from the experts?', pp.15–20. In *Proceedings of a Conference: Bilingualism – Teaching English as a Second Language to Deaf Children*. A LASER publication.

BAKER R. & CHILD D. (1993) 'Communication approaches used in schools for the deaf in the UK – a follow-up study'. *Journal of the British Association of Teachers of the Deaf*, Vol. 17, No. 2, pp.36–47.

BALDWIN J.M. (1897) *Social and Ethical Interpretations in Mental Development*. New York: Macmillan.

BALLANTYNE J. (1970) *Deafness*. (2nd edn) J. & A. Churchill. (1st published 1960.)

BAMFORD J. (1988) 'Visual reinforcement audiometry', pp.117–35. In McCormick (1988a).

BANDURA A. (1969) 'Social-learning theory of identificatory processes', pp.213–62. In Goslin (1969).

BANDURA A. (1977) *Social Learning Theory*. Englewood Cliffs, NJ: Prentice-Hall.

BANDURA A. & WALTERS R.H. (1963) *Social Learning and Personality Development*. New York: Holt, Rinehart & Winston.

BARTSCH K. & WELLMAN H. (1989) 'Young children's attribution of action to beliefs and desires'. *Child Development*, Vol. 60, No. 4, pp.946–64.

BATES A. & HOLSGROVE G. (1979) 'The Phonic Ear'. *Journal of the British Association of Teachers of the Deaf*, Vol. 3, No. 5, pp.164–70.

BATESON G., JACKSON D.D., HALEY J., & WEAKLAND J. (1976) 'Toward a theory of schizophrenia 1956', pp.3–22. In C.E. Sluzki and D.C. Ransom (eds) *Double-bind: The Foundation of the Communicational Approach to the Family*. New York: Grune and Stratton.

BAUMEISTER R.F., TICE D.M. & HUTTON D.G. (1989) 'Self-presentational motivations and personality differences in self-esteem'. *Journal of Personality*, Vol. 57, pp.547–79.

BEAGLEY H.A. (1981) *Audiology and Audiological Medicine. Volume I*. Oxford University Press.

BEEGHLY M., BRETHERTON I., MERVIS C.B. (1986) 'Mothers' internal state language to toddlers'. *British Journal of Developmental Psychology*, Vol. 4, Pt 3, pp.247–61.

BELL R.Q. (1971) 'Stimulus control of parent or caretaker behaviour by offspring'. *Developmental Psychology*, Vol. 4, No. 1, pp.63–72.

BELL R.Q. (1974) 'Contributions of human infants to caregiving and social interaction'. In M. Lewis and L. Rosenblum (eds) *The Effect of the Infant on its Caregiver*. New York: Wiley.

BELLINGER D. (1980) 'Consistency in the pattern of change in mothers' speech: some discriminant analysis'. *Journal of Child Language*, Vol. 7, No. 3, pp.469–87.

BELLMAN S. (1987) 'Testing and screening of hearing', Ch.6, pp.65–79. In Evans

(1987).

BELLUGI U. (1976) 'Attitudes towards sign language: is there a need for change?'. *Supplement to the British Deaf News,* October.

BELLUGI U. and KLIMA E.S. (1982) 'The acquisition of three morphological systems in American Sign Language'. *Papers and Reports on Child Language Development,* Vol. 21, pp.1–35. Stanford, CA: Stanford University.

BENTLER R.A., ELFENBEIN J.L. & SCHUM R.L. (1984) 'Identical deaf triplets: audiological, speech-language, and psychological characteristics'. *American Annals of the Deaf,* Vol. 129, No. 6, pp.466–80.

BENTOVIM A. (1976) 'Disobedience and violent behaviour in children: family pathology and family treatment'. *British Medical Journal,* Vol. 1, No. 6015, pp.947–9.

BERGER C.R. (1975) 'Proactive and retroactive attribution processes in interpersonal communicaton'. *Human Communication Research,* Vol. 2, pp.33–50.

BERGER C.R. (1979) 'Beyond initial interaction: uncertainty, understanding and the development of interpersonal relationships'. In H. Giles and R. St Clair (eds) *Language and Social Psychology.* Oxford: Basil Blackwell.

BERGER C.R. & BRADAC J.J. (1982) *Language and Social Knowledge: Uncertainty in Interpersonal Relations.* Edward Arnold.

BERGER P. and BERGER B. (1978) *Sociology A Biographical Approach.* Harmondsworth: Penguin.

BERGER P. & LUCKMAN T. (1967) *The Social Construction of Reality.* Harmondsworth: Allen Lane

BERGSON H. (1938) *Essai sur les données immediates de la conscience.* Paris: F. Alcan (English translation by R.L. Pogson *Time and Free Will.* New York: Macmillan, 1913). Cited in Wagner (1975).

BERNAL J. (1974) 'Attachment: some problems and possibilities', pp.153–65. In M.P.M. Richards (ed.) *The Integration of a Child Into a Social World.* Cambridge University Press.

BERNSTEIN B. (1971) *Class Codes and Control (Vol 1).* Routledge and Kegan Paul.

BERNSTEIN, B. (1973) *Class Codes and Control (Vol II).* Routledge and Kegan Paul.

BEST C.H. & TAYLOR N.B. (1966) *The Physiological Basis of Medical Practice.* (8th edn) E .& S. Livingstone Ltd. (1st published 1937.)

BEZIRGANIAN S., COHEN P. & BROOK J.S. (1993) 'The impact of mother-child interaction on the development of borderline personality disorder'. *American Journal of Psychiatry,* Vol. 150, No. 12, pp.1836–42.

BIGGLESTONE S. (1986) 'Screening babies' hearing: evaluating the Body Spek 2000'. *Health Visitor,* Vol. 59, No. 12, pp.377–8.

BIRDWHISTELL R.L. (1970) *Kinesics and Context: Essays on Body Motion Communication.* University of Pennsylvania Press.

BISHOP D.V.M. (1983) 'Comprehension of English syntax by profoundly deaf children'. *Journal of Child Psychology and Psychiatry,* Vol. 24, No. 3, pp.415–34.

de BLAUW A., DUBBER C., van ROOSMALEN G. & SNOW C.E. (1979) 'Sex and social class differences in early mother–child interactions'. In O.K. Garnica and M.L. Kay (eds) *Language, Children and Society.* Pergamon Press.

BLOOM F. (1965) *Our Deaf Children.* William Heinemann. (1st published 1963.)

BLUMER H. (1969) *Symbolic Interactionism: Perspective and Method.* Englewood Cliffs, NJ: Prentice-Hall.

BOIVIN M. & BÉGIN G. (1989) 'Peer status and self-perception among early elementary school children: the case of the rejected children'. *Child Development,* Vol. 60, No. 3, pp.591–6.

BONVILLIAN J.D. & RICHARDS H.C. (1993) 'The development of hand preference in children's early signing'. *Sign Language Studies,* Vol. 78, pp.1–14.

BORNSTEIN H. (1974) 'Signed English: a manual approach to English language'. *Journal of Speech and Hearing Disorders,* Vol. 39, No. 3, pp.330–43.

BORNSTEIN H., SAULNIER K.L. & HAMILTON L.B. (1980) 'Signed English: a first evaluation'. *American Annuals of the Deaf,* Vol. 125.

BOWLBY J. (1989) 'James Robertson's contribution'. Introduction to the James Robertson Memorial Meeting held at the Tavistock Clinic, Tavistock Centre, London, 17 November 1989. Unpublished.

BRADLEY R.H. & CALDWELL B.M. (1976) 'The relation of infants' home environments to mental test performance at fifty-four months: a follow-up study'. *Child Development,* Vol. 47, No. 4, pp.1172–4.

BRAY J., CRAGG P.A., MACKNIGHT A.D.C., MILLS R.G. & TAYLOR W. (eds) (1989) *Lecture Notes on Human Physiology.* (2nd edn) Oxford: Blackwell Scientific Publications. (1st published 1986.)

BRAZELTON T.B., KOSLOWSKI B. & MARN M. (1974) 'The origins of reciprocity: the early mother–infant interaction'. In M. Lewis & L. Rosenblum (eds) *The Effect of the Infant on its Caregiver.* New York: Wiley.

BREHM S.S., KASSIN S.M. & GIBBONS F.X. (eds) (1981) *Developmental Social Psychology.* Oxford University Press.

BRENNAN M. (1976) 'Can deaf children acquire language?'. *Supplement to the British Deaf News,* February.

BRENNAN M. (1981) 'Grammatical processes in British Sign Language', pp.120–35. In Woll et al (1981).

BRENNAN M. (1989) 'A positive partnership: BSL and English/deaf and hearing'. Report from a paper given at a conference on 4 November 1989: *Bilingualism: Teaching English as a Second Language to Deaf Children. LASERBEAM,* No. 12, Spring 1990.

BRENNAN M., COLVILLE M. & LAWSON L. (1984) *Words in Hand: A Structural Analysis of the Signs of British Sign Language.* Edinburgh: Edinburgh BSL Research Project.

BRILL R.G. (1976) Ch.14, pp.80–6. In RNID (1976).

BRINICH P.M. (1980) 'Childhood deafness and maternal control'. *Journal of Communication Disorders,* Vol. 13, No. 1, pp.75–81.

BROOKS D.N. (1988) 'Acoustic measurement of auditory function', Ch. 9, pp.247–63. In McCormick (1988c).

BROOKS-GUNN J., DUNCAN G.J., KLEBANOV P.K. & SEALAND N. (1993) 'Do neighbourhoods influence child and adolescent development?'. *American Journal of Sociology,* Vol. 99, No. 2, pp.353–95.

BROWN J.D., COLLINS R.L. & SCHMIDT G.W. (1988) 'Self-esteem and direct versus indirect forms of self-enhancement'. *Journal of Personality and Social Psychology,* Vol. 55, No. 3, pp.445–53.

BROWN R. & GILMAN A. (1960) 'The pronouns of power and solidarity', pp.253–76. In T.A. Sebeok (ed.) *Style in Language.* Cambridge, Mass: MIT Press.

BROWNELL C.A. (1990) 'Peer social skills in toddlers: competencies and constraints illustrated by same-age and mixed-age interactions'. *Child Development,* Vol. 61, No. 3, pp.838–48.

BRUNER J.S. (1970) *Poverty and Childhood.* Occasional Paper. Detroit, Mich: Merrill-Palmer Institute.

BRUNER J.S. (1974) 'The organisation of early skilled action', pp.167–84. In Richards (1974).

BRUNER J.S. (1977) 'Early social interaction and language acquisition'. In H.R

Schaffer (ed.) *Studies in Mother–Child Interaction.* London: Academic Press.

BRUNSWICK E. (1943) 'Organismic achievement and environmental probability'. *Psychological Review,* Vol. 50, pp.255–72.

BURTON R.V. (1972) 'Socialization'. Vol. 14, pp.534–44. In *International Encyclopaedia of the Social Sciences.* New York: Macmillan Free Press. (1st published 1968.)

BUSCAGLIA L. (1975) *The Disabled and Their Parents: A Counselling Challenge.* Thorofare, NJ: Charles B. Slack.

CARTWRIGHT D. (1959) 'Lewinian theory as a contemporary systematic framework', pp.7–91. In S. Koch (ed.) *Psychology: The Study of Science.* New York: McGraw-Hill.

CASELLI M.C. (1983) 'Communication to language: deaf children's and hearing children's development compared'. *Sign Language Studies,* Vol. 39, pp.113–44.

CASELLI M.C. (1987) 'Language acquisition by Italian deaf children'. In Kyle (1987).

CAZDEN E. (1972) *Child Language and Education.* New York: Holt, Rinehart & Winston.

CDR (1987) *Communicable Diseases Report: PHLS Surveillance of Antenatal Rubella Susceptibility, Vaccination of Non-Immune Women, and Rubella Infection in Pregnancy.* National Congenital Rubella Surveillance Programme, Department of Paediatrics and Child Health, University of Leeds, Leeds General Infirmary.

CENTER Y. & WARD J. (1987) 'Teachers' attitudes towards the integration of disabled children into regular classes'. *Exceptional Child,* Vol. 34, No. 1, pp.41–56.

CHESS S. (1975) 'Behaviour problems of children with congenital rubella'. In D. Naiman (ed.), *Needs of Emotionally Disturbed Hearing Impaired Children.* New York University, School of Education, Health, Nursing and Art Professions.

CHOMSKY N. (1968) *Language and Mind.* Harcourt Brace and World.

CLARK M.H. (1983) 'An auditory oral approach to the development of conventional communicative competence'. In *Proceedings of the IV British Conference on Audiology, 4–7 September 1983.* London: University College.

COLLIS G.M. (1979) 'Describing the structure of social interaction in infancy'. In M. Bullowa (ed.) *Before Speech: the Beginning of Interpersonal Communication.* Cambridge: Cambridge University Press.

COLLIS G.M. & SCHAFFER H.R. (1975) 'Synchronization of visual attention in mother–infant pairs'. *Journal of Child Psychology and Psychiatry,* Vol. 16, pp.315–20.

CONRAD R. (1979a) *The Deaf School Child.* Harper and Row.

CONRAD R. (1979b) 'Why Sign?' *Journal of the British Association of Teachers of the Deaf,* Vol. 3, No. 3, p.80.

CONRAD R. (1980) 'Let the children choose'. *International Journal of Paediatric Otorhinolaryngology,* Vol. 1, pp.317–29.

CONRAD R. (1981) 'Sign language in education: some consequent problems'. In Woll et al. (1981).

COOPERSMITH S. (1967) *The Antecedents of Self-Esteem.* W.H. Freeman.

CORCORAN A.L. (1987) 'Hearing Aids', Ch.13, pp.481–505. In D. Stephens (ed.) *Scott-Brown's Otolaryngology: Adult Audiology.* (5th edn) Butterworth.

CORNETT O.R. (1967) 'Cued speech'. *American Annals of the Deaf,* Vol. 112, pp.3–13.

CORSARO W.A. (1981) 'Friendship in the nursery school: social organization in a peer environment', pp.207–41. In S.R. Asher & J.M. Gottman (eds) *The Development of Children's Friendships.* Cambridge University Press.

COTTRELL L.S. (1969) 'Interpersonal interaction and the development of the self', pp.543–70. In Goslin (1969).

COURTMAN-DAVIES M. (1979) *Your Deaf Child's Speech and Language.* The Bodley Head.

CRAIG E.M. (1976) 'A supplement to the spoken word – the Paget Gorman sign system', Ch.9. In RNID (1976).

CRAMER D. (1990) 'Self-esteem and close relationships: a statistical refinement'. *British Journal of Social Psychology*, Vol. 29, Pt 2, pp.189–91.

CRANDELL K.E. (1978) 'Inflectional morphemes in the manual English of young hearing-impaired children and their mothers'. *Journal of Speech and Hearing Research*, Vol. 21, No. 2, pp.372–86.

CRAWFORD M. & KEIR M. (1989) 'From BSL to English – bridging the gap', pp.28–34. In *Proceedings of a Conference: Bilingualism – Teaching English as a Second Language to Deaf Children*. A LASER publication.

CROMER R. (1979) 'The strengths of the weak form of the cognition hypothesis for language acquisition', pp.102–30. In V. Lee (ed.) *Language Development*. Croom Helm.

CROSS T.G. (1977) 'Mothers' speech adjustments: the contributions of selected child listener variables'. In C. Snow and C. Ferguson (eds) *Talking to Children: Language Input and Acquisition*. Cambridge University Press.

CRYSTAL D. (1976) *Child Language, Learning and Linguistics*. Edward Arnold.

CUMMING C.E. (1982) 'Counseling with parents of hearing impaired children'. Unpublished manuscript. Edmonton: University of Alberta.

DALE D.M.C. (1972) *Deaf Children at Home and at School*. (4th edn) University of London Press Ltd. (1st published 1967.)

DAMON W. (1977) *The Social World of the Child*. Jossey-Bass.

DANZIGER K. (1978) *Socialization*. Harmondsworth: Penguin. (1st published 1971.)

DAUNT W. (1990) 'How to change from Total Communication to bilingualism'. Report from a paper given at a conference on 4 November 1989: *Bilingualism: Teaching English as a Second Language to Deaf Children. LASERBEAM*, No. 12, Spring 1990.

DAVIS A. (1983) 'Hearing disorders in the population: first phase findings of the MRC National Study of Hearing'. In M.E. Lutman and M.P. Haggard (eds) *Hearing Science and Hearing Disorders*. London: Academic Press.

DAVIS C. (1976) Ch.11, pp.60–6. In RNID (1976).

DAVIS M. (1989) 'Access to the national curriculum for deaf children'. LASERBEAM, No. 11, Summer 1989, pp.3–7.

DEE A., RAPIN I. & RUBEN R.J. (1982) 'Speech and language development in a parent–infant Total Communication programme'. *Annals of Otology, Rhinology and Laryngology*, Vol. 91 (supplement 97), pp.62–72.

DENMARK C. (1990) 'Is English the first language of deaf children?' Report from a talk (with voice-over) given at a conference on 4 November 1989: *Bilingualism: Teaching English as a Second Language to Deaf Childraen, LASERBEAM*, No. 12, Spring 1990.

DENMARK J. (1976) 'Methods of communication in the education of deaf children', Ch.13 , pp.73–9. In RNID (1976).

DENMARK J.C. (1966) 'Mental illness and early profound deafness'. *British Journal of Medical Psychology*, Vol. 39, pp.117–24.

DENMARK J.C. (1982) 'Some psychological aspects of profound early childhood deafness'. In *Research Highlights 2: Normalisation*. Department of Social Work, University of Aberdeen, Kings College, Aberdeen.

DENMARK J.C. & ELDRIDGE R.W. (1969) 'Psychiatric services for the deaf'. *Lancet*, Vol. 11, No. 7614, 2 August.

DENMARK J.C., RODDA M., ABEL R.A., SKELTON U., ELRIDGE R.W., WARREN F. & GORDON A. (1979) *A Word in Deaf Ears*. Royal National Institute for the Deaf.

DENMARK J.C. & WARREN F. (1972) 'A psychiatric unit for the deaf'. *British Journal of Psychiatry*, Vol. 120, No. 557, pp.423–8.

DENSHAM J. (1990) 'Children with impaired hearing: their socialization and modes of communication'. Unpublished PhD thesis, University of Hertfordshire.

DENSHAM J. (1992) 'Deaf children: professional decisions and life outcomes'. Unpublished paper presented at the British Sociological Association Medical Sociology Group and European Society of Medical Sociology Conference on Health in Europe: Diversity, Integration and Change. University of Edinburgh, 18–21 September.

DENTON D.M. (1976) 'The Philosophy of Total Communication'. *Supplement to the British Deaf News*, August.

DES (1968) *The Education of Deaf Children: the Possible Place of Fingerspelling and Signing* (The Lewis Report). Department of Education and Science. London: HMSO.

DES (1985) *Educational Provision for Children with Special Needs.* Department for Education and Science. London: HMSO.

DES/WELSH OFFICE (1988) *Education Statistics.* Department of Education and Science. London: HMSO.

DEUCHAR M. (1984) *British Sign Language.* Routledge and Kegan Paul.

DEUTSCH M. (1972) 'Field theory', pp.406 – 7. In Burton (1972).

DHSS (1977) Advisory Committee on Services for Hearing-Impaired People (ACSHIP): *Report of the subcommittee appointed to consider the role of social services in the care of the deaf of all ages.* London: DHSS.

DHSS (1986) *Register of Handicapped Persons. Registers of the Deaf and Hard of Hearing at 31 March 1986.* Personal Social Services: Local Authority Statistics. London: HMSO.

DI CARLO I.M. (1964) *The Deaf.* Englewood Cliffs, NJ: Prentice-Hall.

DI FRANCESCA S. (1972) *Academic Achievement Test Results of a National Testing Program for Hearing Impaired Students – United States: Spring 1971.* Series D, No. 9. Washington DC: Gallaudet College, Office of Demographic Studies.

DI VESTA F. (1974) *Language Learning and Cognitive Processes.* Belmont, Calif: Wadsworth.

DIENER C.I. & DWECK C.S. (1978) 'An analysis of learned helplessness: continuous changes in performance strategy, and achievement cognitions following failure'. *Journal of Personality and Social Psychology*, Vol. 36, No. 3, pp.451–62.

DIENER C.I. & DWECK C.S. (1980) 'An analysis of learned helplessness: (II) the processing of success'. *Journal of Personality and Social Psychology*, Vol. 39, No. 5, pp.940–52.

DIMMOCK A. (1981) Foreword to Montgomery (1981a).

DODGE K.A., PETTIT G., MCCLASKEY C.L. & BROWN M.M. (1986) *Social Competence in Children. Monographs of the Society for Research in Child Development,* Serial No. 215, Vol. 51, No. 2.

DORLANDS ILLUSTRATED MEDICAL DICTIONARY (1985) (26th edn). W.B. Saunders.

DOUGLAS J.W.B. (1964) *The Home and The School: A Study of Ability and Attainment in the Primary School.* Granada.

DOWDNEY L., SKUSE D., RUTTER M., QUINTON D. & MRAZEK (1985) 'The nature and quality of parenting provided by women raised in institutions'. *Journal of Child Psychology and Psychiatry.* Vol. 26, pp.599–625.

DOYLE P. (1988) *The God Squad.* Corgi.

DREVER J. (1974) *A Dictionary of Psychology.* Revised by H. Wallerstein. (1st published 1952.) Harmondsworth: Penguin.

DUNN J. & KENDRICK C. (1979) 'Interaction between young siblings in the context of family relationships', Ch.8, pp.143–68. In Lewis & Rosenblum (1979).

DURKHEIM E. (1902) *On Morality and Society. Selected Writings.* Edited with an introduction by R.N. Bellah (1973). Chicago: University of Chicago Press.

DURKHEIM E. & MAUSS M. (1903) *Primitive Classifications.* (Developed 1901–2. 1st published in English 1963, translated from the French and edited by R. Needham.) Cohen & West (1970).

DWECK C.S. (1975) 'The role of expectations and attributions in the alleviation of learned helplessness'. *Journal of Personality and Social Psychology,* Vol. 31, No. 4, pp.674–85.

DWECK C.S. & REPUCCI N.D. (1973) 'Learned helplessness and reinforcement responsibility in children'. *Journal of Personality and Social Psychology,* Vol. 25, No. 1, pp.109–16.

EDWARDS V. (1987) 'Clever people speak proper'. *The Guardian,* 5 May. (V.W. Edwards, Department of Applied Linguistics, Birkbeck College, 43 Gordon Square, London WC1 0PD.)

EEC (1988) 'Resolution on sign languages for the deaf'. *Official Journal of the European Communities.* Doc A2–302/87. ISSN 0378–6986, C187, Vol. 31, 18 July.

EMERTON R.G. & ROTHMAN G. (1978) 'Attitudes towards deafness: hearing students at a hearing and deaf college'. *American Annals of the Deaf,* Vol. 123, pp.588–93.

ENRIGHT F.P. (1982) 'A profile of counselling skills applied in the preschool setting by peripatetic teachers of the deaf'. *Journal of the British Association of Teachers of the Deaf,* Vol. 6, No. 4, pp.94–100.

EVANS J.N.G. (ed.) (1987) *Scott-Brown's Otolaryngology: Paediatric Otolaryngology.* (5th edn) Butterworth International Edition.

EVANS P.I.P. (1988) 'Hearing aid systems', Ch.10, pp.265–97. In McCormick (1988a).

EWING A.W.G. & EWING E.C. (1964) *Teaching Deaf Children to Talk.* Manchester University Press.

FARB P. (1977) *Word Play: What Happens When People Talk.* Hodder & Stoughton. (1st published in the UK by Jonathan Cape, 1974.)

FINCHAM F.D., DIENER C.I. & HOKODA A. (1987) 'Attributional style and learned helplessness'. *British Journal of Social Psychology,* Vol. 26, Pt 1, pp.1–7.

FINCHAM F.D. & HOKODA A.J. (1987) 'Learned helplessness in social situations and sociometric status'. *European Journal of Social Psychology,* Vol. 17, No. 1, pp.95–111.

FINCHAM F.D., HOKODA A.J. & SANDERS R. Jr (1989) 'Learned helplessness, test anxiety and academic achievement: a longitudinal analysis'. *Child Development,* Vol. 60, No. 1, pp.138–45.

FISHER B. (1965) 'The social and emotional adjustment of children with impaired hearing attending ordinary classes'. M.Ed. thesis, University of Manchester.

FISHMAN J. (1972) *The Sociology of Language: An Interdisciplinary Social Science Approach to Language in Society.* Rowley, Mass: Newbury House Publishers.

FISHMAN J. (1975) *Sociolinguistics: A Brief Introduction.* Rowley, Mass: Newbury House Publishers (4th printing, 1st published 1970.)

FITOURI A. (1983) 'Working with young bilingual children'. *Early Child Development and Care,* Vol. 10, pp.283–92.

FLETCHER L. (1987) 'Educating deaf children: the bilingual option – a parent's view', pp.10–13. In *Proceedings of a Conference: Educating the Deaf Child, The Bilingual Option.* A LASER publication. (The Language of Sign as an Educational Resource.)

FOLVEN R.J. & BONVILLIAN J.D. (1991) 'The transition from non-referential to referential language in children acquiring American Sign Language'. *Developmental Psychology*, Vol. 27, No. 5, pp.806–16.

FOUCAULT M. (1971) *Madness and Civilization: A History of Insanity in the Age of Reason.* (Translated from the French by Richard Howard.) Tavistock Publications. (Originally published as *Histoire de la Folie*, Paris: Librairie Pion, 1961.)

FRASER G.R. (1987) 'The genetics of deafness', Ch.3, pp.26–34. In Evans (1987).

FREELAND A. (1989) *Deafness: The Facts.* Oxford University Press.

FREEMAN R.D. (1976) 'Some psychiatric reflections on the controversy over methods of communication in the life of the deaf', pp.110–18. In RNID (1976).

FREEMAN R.D. (1977) 'Psychiatric aspects of sensory disorders and intervention', pp.275–304. In P.J. Graham (ed.) *Epidemiological Approaches in Child Psychiatry.* New York: Academic Press.

FREEMAN R.D., CARBIN C.F. & BOESE R.J. (1981) *Can't Your Child Hear?* Croom Helm.

FREEMAN R.D., MALKIN S.F. & HASTINGS J.O. (1975) 'Psychosocial problems of deaf children and their families: a comparative study'. *American Annals of the Deaf,* Vol. 120, pp.391–405.

FREUD S. (1940) *Outline of Psychoanalysis Vol. XXIII.* (Standard edn, 1964) Hogarth Press.

FREUD S. (1965) *New Introductory Lectures on Psychoanalysis.* New York: Norton. (1st published 1933.)

FRIDMAN R. (1980) 'Proto-rhythms from non-verbal to language and musical acquisition'. In M.R. Key (ed.) *The Relationship of Verbal and Non-verbal Communication.* The Hague: Mouton.

FRY D. (1968) 'The development of the phonological system in the normal and deaf child'. In F. Smith & G.A. Miller (eds) *The Genesis of Language: A Psycholinguistic Approach.* Cambridge, Mass: MIT Press.

FRY D. (1979) 'How did we learn to do it?' In V. Lee (ed.) *Language Development.* Croom Helm.

FULTON B. & GOTTESMAN D.J. (1980) 'Anticipatory grief: a psychosocial concept reconsidered'. *British Journal of Psychiatry,* Vol. 137, pp.45–54.

FURFEY P.H. & HARTE T.J. (1964) *Interaction of Deaf and Hearing in Frederick County Maryland.* Washington DC: Catholic University of America Press.

FURTH H.G. (1961) 'The influence of language on the development of concept formation in deaf children'. *Journal of Abnormal and Social Psychology,* Vol. 63, pp.386–9.

FURTH H.G. (1966) *Thinking Without Language: Psychological Implications of Deafness.* Collier-Macmillan.

FURTH H.G. (1973) *Deafness and Learning: A Psychosocial Approach.* Belmont, Calif: Wadsworth.

FURTH H.G. (1978) 'Young children's understanding of society'. In H. McGurk (ed.) *Issues in Childhood Social Development.* Methuen.

GARRETSON M.D. (1976) 'Total Communication'. *Volta Review,* Vol. 78, No. 2, pp.88–95.

GARRETSON M.D. (1981) 'The unwritten curriculum', pp.153–164. In Montgomery (1981a).

GEERS A.E. (1985) 'Assessment of hearing impaired children: determining typical and optimal levels of performance', Ch.3, pp.57–82. In Powell et al (1985).

GEERS A., MOOG J. & SCHICK R. (1984) 'Acquisition of spoken and signed English by profoundly deaf children'. *Journal of Speech and Hearing Disorders,* Vol. 49, No. 4, pp.378–88.

GEERS A.E. & SCHICK B. (1988) 'Acquisition of spoken and signed English by hearing-impaired children of hearing-impaired or hearing parents'. *Journal of Speech and Hearing Disorders*, Vol. 53, No. 2, pp.136–43.

GENISHI C. & DYSON A.H. (1984) *Language Assessment in the Early Years*. Norwood, NJ: Ablex.

GERGEN K.J. & GERGEN M.M. (1981) *Social Psychology*. New York: Harcourt Brace Jovanovich.

GIBBIN K.P. (1988) 'Otological considerations in the first five years of life', pp.37–68. In McCormick (ed.) (1988c).

GOETZ T.E. & DWECK C.S. (1980) 'Learned helplessness in social situations'. *Journal of Personality and Social Psychology*, Vol. 39, No. 2, pp.246–55.

GOFFMAN E. (1973) *Stigma*. Englewood Cliffs, NJ: Prentice-Hall (1st published 1963.)

GOFFMAN E. (1974) *Asylums*. Harmondsworth: Penguin. (1st published by Anchor Books, Doubleday, 1961.)

GOFFMAN E. (1976) *Presentation of Self in Everyday Life*. Harmondsworth: Allen Lane. (1st published 1959.)

GOLDBERG S. (1988) 'Risk factors in infant–mother attachment'. *Canadian Journal of Psychology*, Vol. 42, No. 2, pp.173–88.

GOLDWIN-MEADOW S. & FELDMAN H. (1975) 'The creation of a communication system: a study of deaf children of hearing parents'. *Sign Language Studies*, Vol. 8, pp.225–34.

GOLDWIN-MEADOW S. & FELDMAN H. (1977) 'The development of language-like communication without a language model'. *Science*, Vol. 197, pp.401–03.

GOODNOW J.J. (1988) 'Parents' ideas, actions and feelings: models and methods from developmental and social psychology'. *Child Development*, Vol. 59, No. 2, pp.286–320.

GOODRIDGE F. (1960) *The Language of the Silent World*. British Deaf and Dumb Association.

GOPNIK A. (1990) 'Developing the idea of intentionality: children's theories of mind'. *Canadian Journal of Philosophy*, Vol. 20, No. 1, pp.89–114.

GOPNIK A & GRAF P. (1988) 'Knowing how you know: young children's ability to identify and remember the sources of their beliefs'. *Child Development*, Vol. 59, No. 5, pp.1366–71.

GORDON S. (1975) *Living Fully: A Guide for Young People with a Handicap; their Parents, their Teachers and Professionals*. New York: John Day.

GORMAN P. & CRAIG E.M. (1970) 'The Paget Gorman systematic sign system'. In *Proceedings of the International Conference on the Education of the Deaf (ICOED)*. Stockholm: University of Scandinavia.

GOSLIN D.A. (ed.) (1969) *Handbook of Socialization Theory and Research*. Chicago: Rand McNally.

GRAHAM P. (1986) *Child Psychiatry: A Developmental Approach*. Oxford Medical Publications.

GRANT J. (1987) *The Hearing Impaired: Birth to Six*. Boston, Mass: College-Hill.

GREENBERG M. (1980) 'Social interaction between deaf preschoolers and their mothers'. *Developmental Psychology*, Vol. 16, pp.465–74.

GREENE J. (1986) *Language Understanding: A Cognitive Approach*. Milton Keynes: Open University Press.

GREGORY S. (1976) *The Deaf Child and His Family*. George Allen & Unwin.

GREGORY S. & BARLOW S. (1986) 'Interaction between deaf babies and their deaf and hearing mothers'. Unpublished paper presented to the Language

Development and Sign Language Workshop, Bristol, November. (Quoted with permission from Susan Gregory, The Open University, Milton Keynes.)

GREGORY S. & BISHOP J. (1989) 'The integration of deaf children into ordinary schools: a research report'. *Journal of the British Association of Teachers of the Deaf*, Vol. 13, No. 1, pp.1–6.

GREGORY S. & MOGFORD K. (1981) 'Early language development in deaf children'. In Woll et al. (1981).

GREGORY S., MOGFORD K. & BISHOP J. (1979) 'Mothers' speech to young hearing-impaired children'. *Teacher of the Deaf*, Vol. 3, No. 2, pp.42–3.

GRIMSHAW A.D. (1977) 'A sociologist's point of view'. In C. Snow and C. Ferguson (eds) *Talking to Children: Language Input and Acquisition*. Cambridge University Press.

GROCE N. (1982) 'Beyond institutions: history of some American deaf; an example from Martha's Vineyard'. In P. Higgins and J. Nash (eds) *Deaf Community and the Deaf Population*. Washington DC: Gallaudet College.

GROSS R. (1970) 'Language used by mothers of deaf children and mothers of hearing children'. *American Annals of the Deaf*, Vol. 115, pp.93–6.

GUINAGH B.J. & JESTER R.E. (1981) 'Long-term effects of infant stimulation programs'. *Advances in Behavioural Pediatrics*, Vol. 2, pp.81–110.

GURNEY R. (1973) *Language, Brain and Interactive Processes*. Edward Arnold.

GUSTATON G. (1980) *Signing Exact English*. Washington DC: Gallaudet College Press.

HALL D.M.B. (ed.) (1989) *Health for All Children: Report of the Joint Working Party on Child Health Surveillance*, (The Hall Report). Oxford University Press.

HALL E.T. (1979) *The Hidden Dimension*. Anchor.

HALLIDAY S. & LESLIE J.C. (1986) 'A longitudinal semi-cross-sectional study of the development of mother–child interaction'. *British Journal of Developmental Psychology*, Vol. 4, Pt 3, pp.211–22.

HANSEN B. (1987) 'Sign language and bilingualism: a focus on an experimental approach to the teaching of deaf children in Denmark', pp.81–8. In Kyle (1987).

HARDY J.B. (1973) 'Foetal consequences of maternal viral infections in pregnancy'. *Archives of Otolaryngology*, Vol. 98, pp.218–27.

HARGREAVES D.J. (1985) 'Socialization', pp.775–6. In A. Kuper and J. Kuper (eds) *The Social Sciences Encyclopaedia*. Routledge and Kegan Paul (1st published 1985.)

HARRIS M., BARRETT M., JONES D. & BROOKES S. (1988) 'Linguistic input and early word meaning', *Journal of Child Language* Vol. 15, pp.77–94.

HARRIS M., CLIBBENS J., CHASIN J. & TIBBITTS R. (1989) 'The social context of early sign language development'. *First Language*, Vol. 9, pp.81–97.

HARRIS M., JONES D., BROOKES S. & GRANT J. (1986) 'Relations between the non-verbal context of maternal speech and rate of language development'. *British Journal of Developmental Psychology*, Vol. 4, Pt 3, pp.261–8.

HARRIS M., JONES D. & GRANT J. (1983) 'The nonverbal context of mothers' speech to infants'. *First Language*, Vol. 4, Pt 1, No. 10, pp.21–30.

HARRIS M., JONES D. & GRANT J. (1984/85) 'The social-interactional context of maternal speech to infants: an explanation for the event-bound nature of early word use?' *First Language* , Vol. 5, Pt 2, No. 14.

HARRIS R.I. (1978) 'Impulse control in deaf children: research and clinical issues', pp.137–56. In L.S. Liben (ed.) *Deaf Children: Developmental Perspectives*. New York: Academic Press.

HART C.H., LADD G.W. & BURLESON B.R. (1990) 'Children's expectations of the outcomes of social strategies: relations with sociometric status and maternal disciplinary styles'. *Child Development,* Vol. 61, No. 1, pp.127–37.

HART J.G. (1985) 'LAWSEQ: its relation to other measures of self-esteem and academic ability'. *British Journal of Educational Psychology,* Vol. 55, pp.167–9.

HASTINGS P. & HAYES B. (1981) *Encouraging Language Development.* Croom Helm.

HAUGEN E. (1962) *Schizoglossia and the Linguistic Norm.* Monograph Series on Languages and Linguistics 15. Washington DC: Georgetown University.

HAY J. (1981) 'Quiet flows the mainstream', pp.341–49. In Montgomery (1981a).

HEAL J. (1989) *Fact and Meaning: Quine and Wittgenstein on Philosophy of Language.* Oxford: Basil Blackwell.

HENDERSON A.S., BYRNE D.G. & DUNCAN-JONES P. (1981) *Neurosis and the Social Environment.* Sydney: Academic Press.

HESS R.D. & SHIPMAN V.C. (1965) 'Early experience on the socialization of cognitive modes in children'. *Child Development,* Vol. 34, No. 4, pp.869–86.

HIGGINS P.C. (1980) *Outsiders in a Hearing World.* Sage Publications.

HILGARD E.R., ATKINSON R.L. & ATKINSON R.C. (1990) *Introduction to Psychology.* (10th edn) New York: Harcourt Brace Jovanovich (1st published 1953.)

HILKE D.D. (1988) 'Infant vocalization and changes in experience'. *Journal of Child Language,* Vol. 15, No. 1, pp.1–15.

HMSO (1889) *Report of the Commission, Vol.1: Report the Royal Commission on the Blind, the Deaf and Dumb and Others of the United Kingdom.* (4 Vols) London: HMSO.

HMSO (1978) *Health Services Commissioner – Annual Report of Session 1977–78.* London: HMSO.

HODGSON K.W. (1953) *The Deaf and Their Problems.* London: Watts.

HOEMANN H.W. (1972) 'The development of communication skills in deaf and hearing children'. *Child Development,* Vol. 43, No. 4, pp.990–1003.

HOLMES M. (1981) 'Segregated in the mainstream', pp.395–404. In Montgomery (1981a).

HOLSGROVE G.J. (1987) 'Integrating children with impaired hearing – attainment of placement information'. Unpublished PhD thesis. Norwich: University of East Anglia.

HOME H.J. (1966) 'The concept of mind'. *International Journal of Psychoanalysis,* Vol. 47, pp.42–9.

HOUGH J. (1983) *Louder Than Words.* Great Ouse Press.

HOWARTH C.I. & WOOD D.J. (1977) 'A research programme on the intellectual development of deaf children'. *Journal of the British Association of Teachers of the Deaf,* Vol. 1, No. 1, pp.5–12.

HUGHES J. (1978) *Sociological Analysis: Methods of Discovery.* Thomas Nelson.

HUSSERL, E. (1928) *Logische Untersuchungen.* (4th ed) Halle: Niemeyer. (An English synopsis of this work is included in M. Farber (1962) *The Foundation of Phenomenology.* New York: Paine-Whitman.)

HUSTON T.L. (1983) 'Power'. In H.H Kelley, E. Berscheid, A. Christensen, J.H. Harvey, T.L. Huston, G. Levinger, E. McClintock, L.A. Peplau and D.R. Peterson (eds) *Close Relationships.* W.H. Freeman.

HYDE M.L. (1987) 'Evoked potential audiometry', Ch.7, pp.80–103. In Evans (1987).

ILLICH I. (1981) *Shadow Work.* Marion Boyars.

INGLEBY D. (1974) 'The psychology of child psychology'. In Richards (1974).

INTERNATIONAL ENCYCLOPAEDIA FOR SOCIAL SCIENCES (1972) (Vols 13 and 14). Gowell Collier and Macmillan (1st published 1968.)

ISO (1981) *Acoustics. Determination of Sound Power Levels of Noise Sources Using Sound Intensity. Measurement at Discrete Point.* International Standards Organization. ISO 9614. (British Standard 7703.)

IVES L.A. (1976) *A Screening of 2060 Hearing Impaired Children in the Midlands and North of England, The Royal Schools for the Deaf, Manchester.* Carlisle: British Deaf Association.

IWAMURA S.G. (1980) *The Verbal Games of Pre-School Children.* Croom Helm.

JAMES W. (1890) *The Principles of Psychology.* New York: Holt.

JARVIK L.F., SALZBERGER R.M. & FALEK A. (1969) 'Deaf persons of outstanding achievement'. In Rainer et al. (1969).

JENKINS S., BAX H. & HART H. (1980) 'Behaviour problems in pre-school children'. *Journal of Child Psychology and Psychiatry,* Vol. 21, No.1, pp.5–17.

JOHNSON J.C. (1962) *Educating Hearing Impaired Children in Ordinary Schools.* Manchester University Press.

JONES K. (1986) 'The social-psychological needs of deaf people'. In Montgomery (1986a).

JORDAN I.K. (1981) *Surdometrica, Vol. III, No. II.* Edinburgh: Scottish Workshop Publications.

JORDAN K. (1986) 'The growth of Total Communication in the United Kingdom', pp.13–20. In Montgomery(1986a).

KATZ L.G. (1980) 'Mothering and teaching – some significant distinctions', pp.47–63. In L. Katz (ed.) *Current Topics in Early Childhood Education,* Vol. 2. Norwood, NJ: Ablex.

KELLMER PRINGLE M.L. (1966) *Social Learning and its Measurement.* Longmans Green.

KELLY G.A. (1955) *The Psychology of Personal Constructs,* (Vols 1 and 2). New York: Norton.

KELLY G.A. (1963) *A Theory of Personality.* New York: Norton.

KENDALL D.C. (1957) [No title.] In A.W.G. Ewing (ed.) *Educational Guidance and the Deaf Child.* Manchester University Press.

KENDALL D.C. (1960) [No title.] In A.W.G. Ewing (ed.) *The Modern Education of Deafness.* Manchester University Press.

KENT R.D., OSBERGER M.J., NETSELL R. & HUSTEDDE C.G. (1987) 'Phonetic development in identical twins differing in auditory function'. *Journal of Speech and Hearing Disorders,* Vol. 52, No. 1, pp.64–75.

KERCKHOFF A.C. (1972) *Socialization and Social Class.* Engelwood Cliffs, NJ: Prentice-Hall.

KERNIS M.H., CORNELL D.P., SUN C., BERRY A. & HARLOW T. (1993) 'There's more to self-esteem than whether it is high or low: the importance of stability of self-esteem'. *Journal of Personality and Social Psychology,* Vol. 65, No. 6, pp.1190–204.

KLEIN G.S. (1962) 'Blindness and isolation'. *Psychoanalytic Study of the Child,* Vol. 17, pp.82–3.

KLIMA E.S. & BELLUGI U. (1979) *The Signs of Language.* Cambridge, Mass: Harvard University Press.

KRAEMER S. (1989) 'A child psychiatrist goes to hospital'. Unpublished paper presented at the James Robertson Memorial Meeting, The Tavistock Clinic, London, 17 November.

KUBLER-ROSS E. (1969) *On Death and Dying.* New York: Macmillan.

KUCZAJ S.A. (1986) 'Discussion: on social interaction as a type of explanation of language development'. *British Journal of Developmental Psychology,* Vol. 4, Pt 3, pp289–99.

KUSCHEL R. (1973) 'The silent inventor: creation of a sign language by the only deaf mute on a Polynesian island'. *Sign Language Studies,* Vol. 3, pp.1–27.

KYLE J. (ed.) (1987) *Sign and School.* Clevedon, Penn: Multilingual Matters.

KYLE J. (1988) Personal Communication. (From a paper, 'Assessing sign language acquisition', presented at the 3rd Conference of the British Association of Teachers of the Deaf and College of Speech Therapists on The Assessment and Development of Communication in the Context of Deafness. Birmingham, 12 March 1988.)

KYLE J.G. & ALLSOP L. (1982) 'Communicating with young deaf people: some issues'. *Journal of the British Association of Teachers of the Deaf,* Vol. 6, No. 3, pp.71–9.

KYLE J.G. & WOLL B. (eds) (1983) *Language in Sign: An International Perspective on Sign Language.* Croom Helm.

KYLE J.G. & WOLL B. (eds) (1988) *Sign Language: The Study of Deaf People and their Language.* Cambridge University Press.

LABOV W. (1972) *Language in the Inner City: Studies in Black English Vernacular.* Philadelphia: University of Pennsylvania Press.

LADD G.W., MUNSON H.L. & MILLER J.K. (1984) 'Social integration of deaf adolescents in secondary-level mainstreamed programs'. *Exceptional Children,* Vol. 50, No. 5, pp.420–8.

LADD P. (1979) 'Communication or dummification', pp.46–51. In Montgomery (1979).

LADD P. (1981) 'The erosion of social and self identity', pp.405–32. In Montgomery (1981a).

LADD P. (1988) 'The modern deaf community'. In Miles (1988).

LADD P. & EDWARDS V.K. (1982) 'British Sign Language and West Indian Creole'. *Sign Language Studies,* Vol. 35, pp.101–26.

LAING R.D. (1959) *The Divided Self.* Tavistock Publications.

LAING R.D. (1961) *Self and Others.* Tavistock Publications.

LAING R.D. (1965) 'Mystification, confusion and conflict'. In I. Boszormenyi-Nagy and J.L. Framo (eds) *Intensive Family Therapy.* New York: Harper and Row.

LAING R.D. (1967) *The Politics of Experience.* Harmondsworth: Penguin.

LAING R.D. (1976) *The Politics of the Family.* Harmondsworth: Penguin. (1st published by CBC Publications, 1969.)

LAING R.D. & ESTERTON A. (1970) *Sanity, Madness and the Family: Families of Schizophrenics.* (2nd edn) Tavistock Publications. (1st published 1964.)

LAKE T. & ACHESON F. (1989) *Room to Listen, Room to Talk: A Beginner's Guide to Analysis, Therapy and Counselling.* Bedford Square Press/BBC Radio 4. (1st published 1988.)

LANE H. (1977) *The Wild Boy of Aveyron.* George Allen & Unwin. (Originally published by Harvard University Press, by 1976.)

LANSDOWN R. (1980) *More Than Sympathy.* Tavistock Publications.

LEDERBERG A.R., CHAPIN S.L., ROSENBLATT V. & VANDELL D.L. (1986) 'Ethnic, gender and age preferences among deaf and hearing preschool peers'. *Child Development,* Vol. 57, No. 2, pp.375–86.

LENNEBERG E.H. (1967) *Biological Foundations of Language.* New York: John Wiley.

LEVITT E. & COHEN S. (1977) 'Parents as teachers: a rationale for involving parents in the education of their young handicapped children', pp.165–78. In L.G. Katz (ed.) *Current Topics in Early Childhood Education (Vol. 1).* Norwood, NJ: Ablex.

LEVY-SHIFF R. & HOFFMAN M.A. (1985) 'Social behaviour of hearing-impaired and normally-hearing preschoolers'. *British Journal of Educational Psychology,* Vol. 55, Pt 2, pp.111–18.

LEWIN K. (1952) In D. Cartwright (ed.) *Field Theory in Social Sciences Selected Theoretical Papers.* Tavistock Publications.

LEWIS A. & LEWIS V. (1987) 'The attitudes of young children towards peers with severe learning difficulties'. *British Journal of Developmental Psychology*, Vol. 5, pp.287–92.

LEWIS M. & FREEDLE R. (1973) 'Mother–infant dyad: the cradle of meaning', pp.127–55. In P. Pliner, L. Krames and T. Alloway (eds) *Communication and Effect: Language and Thought*. New York: Academic Press.

LEWIS M. & ROSENBLUM L.A. (eds) (1979a) *The Child and its Family*. New York and London: Plenum Press.

LEWIS M. & ROSENBLUM L.A. (1979b) 'Introduction: issues in the study of the social network'. In Lewis and Rosenblum (1979a).

LIEVEN E.V.M. (1980) 'Language development in young children: children's speech and speech to children'. Unpublished PhD thesis. New Hall, Cambridge University.

LIEVEN E.V.M. (1982) 'Context, process and progress in young children's speech'. In M. Beveridge (ed.) *Children Thinking Through Language*. Edward Arnold.

LINDESMITH A.R., STRAUSS A.L. & DENZIN N.K. (1975) *Social Psychology*. (4th edn) Dryden Press. (1st published 1949.)

LINDSAY G. & DICKINSON D. (1987) 'Integration of profoundly hearing-impaired children into a nursery setting'. *Journal of the British Association of Teachers of the Deaf*, Vol. 11, No. 1, pp.1–7.

LINTON R. (1947) *The Cultural Background of Personality*. Routledge.

LIPPITT R. (1968) 'Kurt Lewin' pp.266–70. In D.L. Sills (ed.) *International Encyclopaedia of the Social Sciences, Vol. 19*. Macmillan/The Free Press.

LLEWELLYN-JONES M. (1987) 'Bilingualism and the education of deaf children', pp.14–28. In *Proceedings of a Conference: Educating the Deaf Child, Derby, 17 October*. A LASER publication.

LOMAS P. (1968) 'Psychoanalysis – Freudian or existential', pp.116–50. In C. Rycroft, G. Gorer, A. Starr, J. Wren-Lewis and P. Lomas *Psychoanalysis Observed*. Harmondsworth: Penguin. (1st published by Constable, 1966.)

LOWELL E.L. (1959) 'Research in speechreading: some relationships to language development and implications for the classroom teacher', pp. 68–73. *Report of the Proceedings of the 39th Meeting of the Convention of American Instructors of the Deaf*. Washington DC: Gallaudet College.

LUTERMAN D. (1979) *Counseling parents of Hearing Impaired Children*. Boston, Mass: Little, Brown.

LUTERMAN D.M. (ed.) (1986) *Deafness in Perspective*. San Diego, Calif: College-Hill Press.

LYONS J. (1977) *Chomsky*. Harvester.

McCANDLESS B.R. (1969) 'Childhood socialization'. In Goslin (1969).

McCLELLAND D.C. & FRIEDMAN G.A. (1952) 'A cross-cultural study of the relationship between child-training practices and achievement motivation, appearing in folk tales'. In E.E. Swanson, T.M. Necomb and E.L. Hartley (eds). *Readings in Social Psychology*. New York: Holt.

McCORMICK B. (1979) 'Audio-visual discrimination in speech'. *Clinical Otolaryngology*, Vol. 4, pp.355–61.

McCORMICK B. (1988a) 'Behavioural hearing tests 6 months to 5 years', pp.97–115. In McCormick (1988c).

McCORMICK B. (1988b) *Screening for Hearing Impairment in Young Children*. Croom Helm.

McCORMICK B. (ed.) (1988c) *Paediatric Audiology 0–5 Years*. Taylor and Francis.

McCORMICK B., WOOD S.A., COPE Y. & SPAVINS F.M. (1984) 'Analysis of records from an open access audiology service'. *British Journal of Audiology*, Vol. 18, pp.127–32.

McDOUGALL W. (1908) *Introduction to Social Psychology*. Methuen.

McGILLICUDDY-DE LISI A.V., SIGEL I.E. & JOHNSON J.E. (1979) 'The family as a system of mutual influences: parental beliefs, distancing behaviour and children's representational thinking', pp.91–106. In Lewis and Rosenblum (1979a).

McNEIL E.B. (1969) *Human Socialization*. Belmont, Calif: Brooks/Cole.

MACKINNON K. & DENSHAM J. (1989) 'Ethnolinguistic diversity in Britain: policies and practice in school and society'. *Language Culture and Curriculum*, Vol. 2, No. 2, pp.75–89.

MACMAHON B. & PUGH T.F. (1970) *Epidemiology: Principles and Methods*. Boston, Mass: Little, Brown.

MALINOWSKI B. (1927) Section 2 of the Supplement to C.K. Ogden and I.A. Richards, *The Meaning of Meaning*. Routledge and Kegan Paul.

MARCHANT K. (1987) *Sounds Like Skipper*. Headline.

MARKIDES A. (1983) 'National survey on the speech intelligibility of hearing impaired children', pp.47–8. In *Proceedings of the IV British Conference on Audiology, University College, London, 4–7 September 1983*. London: British Society of Audiology.

MARKIDES A (1985) 'Relationships between auditory, visual and audiovisual speech discrimination abilities and speech intelligibility among prelingually hearing impaired children'. *Journal of the British Association of Teachers of the Deaf*, Vol. 9, No. 1, pp.1–6.

MARKIDES A. (1986) 'Age of fitting of hearing aids and speech intelligibility'. *British Journal of Audiology*, Vol. 20, pp.165–7.

MARKIDES A. (1989) 'Integration: the speech intelligibility, friendships and associations of hearing-impaired children in secondary schools'. *Journal of the British Association of Teachers of the Deaf*, Vol. 13, No. 3, pp.63–72.

MARSH W.H., SMITH I.D., BARNES J. & BUTLER S. (1983) 'Self concept: reliability, stability, dimensionality validity and the measurement of change'. *Journal of Educational Psychology*, Vol. 75, pp.772–90.

MARTIN F.N. (1986a) *Introduction to Audiology*. (3rd edn) Englewood Cliffs, NJ: Prentice-Hall. (1st published 1975.)

MARTIN F.N. (1986b) 'Audiology in perspective', Ch.2, pp.15–33. In Luterman (ed.) (1986).

MARTIN J.A.M. (1982) 'Aetiological factors relating to childhood deafness in the European Community'. *Audiology*, Vol. 21, pp.149–58.

MARTIN J.A.M. (1983) 'Normal patterns of early vocalisation and their significance for the deaf child', p.49. In *Proceedings of the IV British Conference on Audiology, University College, London, 4–7 September 1983*. London: British Society of Audiology.

MARTIN J.A.M., BENTLEN O., COLLEY J.R.T., HENNEBERT D., HOLM C., IURATO S., de JONGE G.A., McCULLEN O., MEYER M.L., MOORE W.J. & MORGON A. (1981) 'Childhood deafness in the European Community'. *Scandinavian Audiology*, Vol. 10, pp.165–74.

MARTIN J.A.M. & MOORE W.J. (1979) *Childhood Deafness in the European Community*. Commission of the European Communities. London: HMSO (EUR 6413).

MARTIN M.C. (1979) 'Hearing aids', Ch.28, p.909. In J. Ballantyne and J. Groves (eds) *Scott Brown's Diseases of the Ear, Nose and Throat: The Ear*. (4th edn) Butterworth.

MARTIN M.C. (1981) 'Audiometers', Ch.8. In Beagley (1981).

MARTIN M. & GROVER B. (1986) *Hearing Loss*. Longman.

MASATAKA N. (1992) 'Motherese in a signed language'. *Infant Behaviour and*

Development, Vol. 15, No. 4, pp.453–60.

MASON E.A. (1989) 'Pioneer on the children's ward: a view from America'. Unpublished paper presented at the James Robertson Memorial Meeting, Tavistock Clinic, London, 17 November.

MASON S.M. (1988) 'Electric response audiometry', Ch.7, pp.167–219. In McCormick (1988c).

MASTERTON J.F. and RINSLEY D.B. (1975) 'The borderline syndrome: the role of the mother in the genesis and psychic structure of the borderline personality'. *International Journal of Psychoanalysis,* Vol. 56, pp.163–77.

MAVILYA M. (1971) 'Spontaneous vocalisation and babbling in hearing impaired infants'. In *Proceedings of the International Congress on the Education of the Deaf, Stockholm 1970.* Stockholm: University of Scandinavia.

MEAD G.H. (1934) *Mind, Self and Society.* University of Chicago Press.

MEADOW K. (1980) *Deafness and Child Development.* Edward Arnold.

MEADOW K.P. & MEADOW L. (1971) 'Changing role of perceptions for parents of handicapped children'. *Exceptional Children,* Vol. 38, pp.21–8.

MENNELL S. (1974) *Sociological Theory: User and Unities.* Thomas Nelson.

MENZIES I. (1960) *The Functioning of Social Systems as a Defence Against Anxiety.* Tavistock Publications.

MESSER D.J. (1983) 'The redundancy between adult speech and nonverbal interaction: a contribution to acquisition'. In R.M. Golinkoff (ed.) *The Transition from Prelinguistic to Linguistic Communication.* Hillside, NJ: Erlbaum.

MEYERSON L. (1948) 'Experimental injury: an approach to the dynamics of disability'. *Journal of Social Issues,* Vol. IV, pp.68–71.

MILES D. (1988) *British Sign Language: A Beginners Guide.* BBC Books.

MILLS R.S.L. & RUBIN K.H. (1990) 'Parental beliefs about problematic social behaviours in early childhood'. *Child Development,* Vol. 61, No. 1, pp.138–51.

MINDEL E.D. & VERNON M. (1971) *They Grow in Silence: The Deaf Child and His Family.* Silver Spring, Md: National Association of the Deaf.

MINOLI I. & MORO G. (1985) 'Constraints of intensive care units and follow up studies'. *Acta Otolaryngologica Supplementum,* Vol. 421, pp.62–7.

MISIASZEK J., DOOLING J., GIESEKE M., MELMAN H., MISIASZEK J.G. & JORGENSEN K. (1985) 'Diagnostic considerations in deaf patients'. *Comprehensive Psychiatry,* Vol. 26, No. 6, pp.513–21.

MOELLER M.P. & LUETKE-STAHLMAN B. (1990) 'Parents' use of signing exact English: a descriptive analysis'. *Journal of Speech and Hearing Disorders,* Vol. 55, No. 2, pp.327–88.

MOHAY H. (1982) 'A preliminary description of the communication systems evolved by two deaf children in the absence of a sign language model'. *Sign Language Studies,* Vol. 34, pp.73–90.

MONTGOMERY G. (1976) 'Changing attitudes to communication'. *Supplement to the British Deaf News,* June.

MONTGOMERY G. (ed.) (1979) *Of Sound and Mind: Deafness, Personality and Mental Health.* Papers presented to the Scottish Workshop with the Deaf. Edinburgh: Lindsay & Co. Ltd. (1st published 1978.)

MONTGOMERY G. (ed.) (1981a) *The Integration and Disintegration of the Deaf in Society.* Edinburgh: Scottish Workshop Publications.

MONTGOMERY G. (1981b) 'Alien communication'. *Supplement to the British Deaf News,* March/April.

MONTGOMERY G. (ed.) (1986a) *Beyond Hobson's Choice: The Appraisal of Methods of Teaching Language to Deaf Children.* Edinburgh: Scottish Workshop Publications.

MONTGOMERY G. (1986b) 'A comparison of limited and Total Communication approaches to language attainment of deaf children', pp.45–60. In Montgomery (1986a).

MONTGOMERY J. (1986) 'The normalisation of language development and emotional behaviour through Total Communication'. In Montgomery (1986a).

MOORE B.C.J. (1982) *An Introduction to the Psychology of Hearing.* London: Academic Press.

MOORES D.F., McINTYRE C.K. & WEISS K.L. (1972) *Evaluation of Programs for Hearing Impaired Children.* Minneapolis, Minn: Research, Development and Demonstration Center in Education of Handicapped Children, Department of Health, Education and Welfare.

MORRIS T. (1981) 'Educating hearing-impaired children in normal classes'. In Montgomery (1981a).

MOSES K. (1977) 'Effects of developmental disability on parenting'. In M. Rieff (ed.) *Patterns of Emotional Growth in the Developmentally Disabled Child.* Morton Grove, Ill: Julia Molloy Education Centre.

MOSES K.L. (1985) 'Infant deafness and parental grief: psychosocial early interaction. In Powell et al (1985).

MOSS J. (1987) 'Functional integration: the best of three worlds'. *Journal of the British Association of Teachers of the Deaf,* Vol. 11, No. 1, pp.15–22.

MULLER K. (1978) 'Counselling aspects in the provision of hearing and speech services'. *Hearing Rehabilitation Quarterly,* Vol. 3, No. 4, pp.14–16.

MUNOZ O., BENITEZ-DIAZ L., MARTINEZ M.C. & GUISCAFRE H. (1983) 'Hearing loss after haemophilus influenzae meningitis: follow up study with auditory brainstem potentials'. *Annals of Otology, Rhinology and Laryngology,* Vol. 92, pp.272–5.

MURRAY-PARKES C. (1975) *Bereavement.* Pelican.

MUSSELMAN C.R., LINDSAY P.H. & WILSON A.K. (1988) 'An evaluation of recent trends in preschool programming for hearing-impaired children'. *Journal of Speech and Hearing Disorders,* Vol. 55, pp.71–88.

NAGY W.E. & HERMAN P.A. (1987) 'Breadth and depth of vocabulary knowledge: implications for acquisition and instruction'. In M.G. McKeown and M.E. Curtis (eds) *The Nature of Vocabulary Acquisition.* Hillside, NJ: Erlbaum.

NDCS (1990) *Personal Stereos and Children's Hearing: A Report.* National Deaf Children's Society, January.

NELSON-JONES R. (1982) *The Theory and Practice of Counselling Psychology.* London: Holt, Rinehart and Winston.

NEWTON V.E. (1985) 'Aetiology of bilateral sensori-neural hearing loss in young children'. *Journal of Laryngology and Otology,* Vol. 99, Supplement 10, p.33.

NIENHUYS T.G. & TIKOTIN J.A. (1983) 'Pre-speech communication in hearing and hearing impaired children'. *Journal of the British Association of Teachers of the Deaf,* Vol. 7, No. 6, pp.182–94.

NIX G.W. (1983) 'How total is Total Communication?' *Journal of the British Association of Teachers of the Deaf,* Vol. 7, No. 6, pp.177–94.

NOLAN M. (1983) 'Acoustic feedback: causes and cures'. *Journal of the British Association of Teachers of the Deaf,* Vol. 7, No. 4, pp.13–17.

NOLAN M. (1988) 'Earmoulds', pp.235–347. In McCormick (1988c).

NOLAN M. & TUCKER I.G. (1981) *The Hearing Impaired Child and the Family.* Souvenir Press.

OGDEN C.G. & RICHARDS I.A. (1923) *The Meaning of Meaning.* Routledge and Kegan Paul.

OLÉRON P. (1953) 'Conceptual thinking of the deaf'. *American Annals of the Deaf,* Vol. 98, pp.304–10.

OLLER D.K. & EILERS R.E. (1988) 'The role of audition in infant babbling'. *Child Development,* Vol. 59, No. 2, pp.441–9.

OLUBANJI D. (1981) *Traditional Attitudes to the Handicapped: Annual General Meeting and Conference of the Nigerian Society for Handicapped Children. 19–21 February 1981.* Owerri, Nigeria: Alvan Ikoku College of Education.

OPEN UNIVERSITY (1975) *Generative Linguistics. Language Acquisition: Language and Cognition.* Prepared by D. Stringer, D. Bruce and J. Oates for the Open University Language and Learning Course Team, Unit E262, Blocks 6 and 7. Milton Keynes: The Open University Press. (1st published 1973.)

OSBERGER M.J., ROBBINS A.M., LYBOLT J., KENT R. & PETERS J. (1986) 'Speech evaluation'. In M.J. Osberger (ed.) *Language and Learning Skills in Hearing-Impaired Students.* American Speech and Hearing Association Monographs 23, pp.24–31. Rockville: ASHA.

OSHIMA-TAKANE Y. (1988) 'Children learn from speech not addressed to them: the case of personal pronouns'. *Journal of Child Language,* Vol. 15, No. 1, pp.95–108.

PANNETON COOPER R. & ASLIN R.N. (1989) 'The language environment of the young infant: implications for early perceptual development'. *Canadian Journal of Psychology,* Vol. 43, No. 2, pp.247–65.

PANOU L. & SEWELL D.F. (1981) 'Cerebral lateralisation in the deaf: a bilingual pattern'. *Journal of Multilingual and Multicultural Development,* Vol. 2, No. 1, pp.45–51.

PATTERSON C.H. (1986) *Theories of Counselling and Psychotherapy.* New York: Harper and Row.

PECKHAM C.S. (1986) 'Hearing impairment in childhood'. *British Medical Bulletin,* Vol. 42, No. 2, pp.145–9.

PECKHAM C.S. COLEMAN J.C., HURLEY R., CHIN K.S. & HENDERSON K. (1983) 'Cytomegalovirus infection in pregnancy: preliminary finding from a prospective study'. *Lancet,* Vol. 1, No. 8338, pp.1352–56.

PECKHAM C.S., STARK O., DUDGEON J.A., MARTIN J.A.M. & HAWKINS G. (1987) 'Congenital cytomegalovirus infection: a cause of sensorineural hearing loss'. *Archives of Diseases in Childhood,* Vol. 62, pp.1233–7.

PETITTO L.A. (1987) 'On the autonomy of language and gesture: evidence from the acquisition of personal pronouns in American Sign Language'. *Cognition,* Vol. 27, pp.1–52.

PETITTO L.A. & MARENTETTE P.F. (1991) 'Babbling in the manual mode: evidence for the ontogeny of language'. *Science,* Vol. 251, No. 5000, pp.1493–6.

PIAGET J. (1932) *The Moral Judgement of the Child.* Glencoe, Ill: The Free Press. (1st published 1932.)

PIAGET J. (1951) *Play, Dreams and Imagination in Childhood.* Routledge and Kegan Paul. (1st published 1946.)

PIAGET J. (1953) *The Origin of Intelligence in the Child.* Routledge and Kegan Paul. (1st published 1936.)

PIAGET J. (1968) *The Child's Construction of Reality.* Routledge and Kegan Paul. (1st published 1937.)

PIAGET J. (1971) *The Language and Thought of the Child.* Routledge and Kegan Paul. (1st published 1926.)

PICKLES J.O. (1982) *Introduction to the Physiology of Hearing.* London: Academic Press.

PICKLES J.O. (1987) 'Physiology of the ear', Ch.2. In Wright (1987).

POWELL F., FINITO-HIEBER T., FRIEL-PATTI S. & HENDERSON D. (eds) (1985)

Education of the Hearing Impaired. Taylor & Francis. (Originally published by College Hill Press 1984.)

POWER D.J., WOOD D.J., WOOD H.A. & MACDOUGALL J. (1990) 'Maternal control over conversation with hearing and deaf infants and young children'. *First Language,* Vol. 10, No. 1, Pt 28, pp.19–35.

PRIDE J.B. (1974) *The Social Meaning of Language*. (2nd edn) Oxford University Press. (1st published 1971.)

PRITCHARD D.G. (1970) *Education and the Handicapped 1760–1960*. (3rd edn) Routledge and Kegan Paul. (1st published 1963.)

QUIGLEY S.P. (1969) *The Influence of Fingerspelling on the Development of Language Communication, and Educational Achievement in Deaf Children*. Urbana, Ill: University of Illinois, Institute for Research on Exceptional Children.

QUIGLEY S.P. & PAUL P.V. (1984) *Language and Deafness.* San Diego, Calif: College-Hill.

QUIGLEY S.P., WILBUR R.B. & MONTANELLI D.S. (1974) 'Question formation in the language of deaf students'. *Journal of Speech and Hearing Research,* Vol. 17, No. 4, pp.699–713.

QUINTON D. & RUTTER M. (1976) 'Early hospital admissions and later disturbances of behaviour: an attempted replication of Douglas's findings'. *Developmental Medicine and Child Neurology,* Vol. 18, pp.447–59.

RAINER J.D. & ALTSCHULER K.Z. (1966) *Comprehensive Mental Health Services for the Deaf.* New York: New York State Psychiatric Institute, Columbia University.

RAINER J.D., ALTSCHULER K.Z. & KALLMAN F.J. (eds) (1969) *Family and Mental Health Problems in a Deaf Population.* (2nd edn) Springfield, Ill: C.C. Thomas. (1st published 1963.)

RAWLINGS B.W. (1971) *Summary of Selected Characteristics of Hearing Impaired Students – United States: 1968–69*. Series D, No. 5, Washington DC: Gallaudet College, Office of Demographic Studies.

REED M. (1956) 'The deaf child and the family'. *Talk,* Vol. 14, Winter, pp.14–18.

REED M. (1976) 'Communication in deaf education', Ch.6. In RNID (1976).

REED M. (1981) 'The strategy of integration'. In Montgomery (1981a).

REES J. (1983) *Sing a Song of Silence.* Kensal Press.

REEVES J.K. (1976) 'The whole personality approach to oralism in the education of the deaf'. In RNID (1976).

REILLY J.S., ZUKOW P.G. & GREENFIELD P.M. (1984) 'Facilitating the transition from sensorimotor to linguistic communication during the one word period'. In A. Lock and E. Fisher (eds) *Language Development.* Croom Helm.

RHEINGOLD H.L. (1969) 'The social and socializing infant', pp.779–90. In Goslin (1969).

RICHARDS M.P.M. (1974) *The Integration of a Child into a Social World.* Cambridge University Press.

RICHMAN N., STEVENSON J.E. & GRAHAM P.J. (1975) 'Prevalence of behaviour problems in three year old children: an epidemiological study in a London borough'. *Journal of Child Psychology and Psychiatry,* Vol.16, pp.277–87.

RICHMAN N., STEVENSON J.E. & GRAHAM P.J. (1982) *Pre-school to School: A Behavioural Study.* London: Academic Press.

RITCHIE J.M. (1930) *Concerning the Blind.* Edinburgh: Oliver & Boyd.

RNID (1976) *Methods of Communication Currently Used in the Education of Deaf Children.* Royal National Institute for the Deaf.

RNID (1981) *Sign and Say.* Royal National Institute for the Deaf.

ROBBINS S.D. (1963) *A Dictionary of Speech Pathology and Therapy.* Cambridge, Mass:

Sci-Art Publishers.

ROBERTSON J. (1958) *Young Children in Hospital.* Tavistock Publications.

RODDA M. & GROVE C. (1987) *Language, Cognition and Deafness.* London: Erlbaum.

ROGERS C. (1978) 'The child's perception of other people'. In H. McGurk (ed.) *Issues in Childhood Social Development.* Methuen.

ROGERS C.R. (1942) *Counseling and Psychotherapy.* Boston, Mass: Houghton Mifflin.

ROGERS C.R. (1977) *On Becoming a Person: A Therapist's View of Psychotherapy.* Constable. (1st published 1961.)

ROGERS C.R. (1987) *Client-Centered Therapy.* Constable. (1st published 1951.)

ROKEACH M. (1972) *Beliefs, Attitudes and Values.* (4th edn) San Francisco: Jossey-Bass. (1st published 1968.)

ROSEN B.C. (1956) 'The achievement syndrome: a psychocultural dimension of social stratification'. *American Sociological Review,* Vol. 21, pp.203–11.

ROSEN B.C. & D'ANDRADE R. (1973) 'The psychological origins of achievement motivation'. In Zigler and Child (1973).

ROSEN H. (1980) 'Linguistic diversity in London schools', pp.46–75. In A.K. Pugh, V.J. Lee & J. Swann (eds) *Language and Language Use.* Heinemann Educational Books /Open University.

ROSENBERG M.E. (1982) *Sound and Hearing.* Edward Arnold.

ROSENBLOOM L. (1987) 'Development and disorders of language: hearing loss'. In Evans (1987).

ROSENHAN D.L. (1973) 'On being sane in insane places'. *Science,* Vol. 179, pp.250–8.

ROSS M. (1990) 'Implications of delay in detection and management of deafness'. *Volta Review,* Vol. 92, No. 2, pp.69–79.

RUBIN K.H. & MILLS R.S.L. (1988) 'The many faces of social isolation in childhood'. *Journal of Consultancy and Clinical Psychology, Vol.* 56, pp.916–924.

RUBIN Z. (1980) *Children's Friendships.* Fontana.

SAHAKIAN W.S. (ed.) (1969) *Psychotherapy and Counseling: Studies in Technique.* Chicago: Rand McNally.

SAINSBURY S. (1986) *Deaf Worlds.* Hutchinson.

SACKS O. (1990) *Seeing Voices.* Picador.

SANCHO J., HUGHES E., DAVIS A. & HAGGARD M. (1988) 'Epidemiological basis for screening hearing', p.1–35. In McCormick (1988c).

SAPIR E. (1966) *Culture, Language and Personality.* Berkeley: University of California Press.

SCHAFFER H.R. (1986) 'Child psychology: the future'. *Journal of Child Psychology and Psychiatry,* Vol. 27, No. 6, pp.761–79.

SCHAFFER H.R. & COLLIS G.M. (1986) 'Parental responsiveness and child behaviour'. In W. Sluckin and M. Herbert (eds) *Parental Behaviour in Animals and Humans.* Oxford: Basil Blackwell.

SCHAFFER H.R. & CROOK C.K. (1978) 'The role of the mother in early social development'. In H. McGurk (ed.) *Issues in Childhood Social Development.* Methuen.

SCHAFFER H.R. & EMERSON P.E. (1973) 'The development of social attachments in infancy', pp.301–18. In Zigler and Child (1973).

SCHEFF T. (1967) *Being Mentally Ill.* Chicago: Aldine Books.

SCHEIN J.D. (1980) 'Educating hearing impaired children to become emotionally well-adjusted adults'. *The Journal of the Association of Canadian Educators of the Hearing Impaired,* Vol. 7, pp.3–9.

SCHEIN J.D. & DELK M.T. (1974) *The Deaf Population of the United States.* Silver Spring, Md: National Association of the Deaf.

SCHERER K.R. (1979) 'Voice and speech correlates of perceived social influence in simulated juries', pp.88–120. In H. Giles & R. StClair (eds) *Language and Social Psychology*. Oxford: Basil Blackwell.

SCHIFF-MYERS N.B. & KLEIN H.B. (1985) 'Some phonological characteristics of the speech of normal hearing children of deaf parents'. *Journal of Speech and Hearing Research*, Vol. 28, No. 4, pp.466–74.

SCHLESINGER H.S. (1976) 'Emotional support for parents'. In D.L. Lillie, P.L. Trohanis & K.W. Goia (eds) *Teaching Parents to Teach*. New York: Walker.

SCHLESINGER H.S. (1978) 'The effects of deafness on childhood development: an Eriksonian perspective', pp.157–69. In L.S. Liben (ed.) *Deaf Children: Developmental Perspectives*. New York: Academic Press.

SCHLESINGER H.S. (1985) 'Deafness, mental health and language'. In Powell et al (1985).

SCHLESINGER H.S. (1986) 'Total Communication in perspective', Ch.5, pp.87–116. In Luterman (1986).

SCHLESINGER H.S. & MEADOW K.P. (1972) *Sound and Sign: Childhood Deafness and Mental Health*. Berkeley: University of California Press.

SCHMITT P. (1966) 'Language instruction for the deaf'. In S.P. Quigley (ed.) *Language Acquisition*. Volta Review (Reprint No. 852.)

SCHUTZ A. (1972) *The Phenomenology of the Social World*. (Translated by G. Walsh and F. Lehnert.) Heinemann Educational Books. (1st published 1967.) (Originally published in German under the title *Der Sinnhafte Aufbau der Sozialen Welt*, 1932. Vienna: Julius Springer.)

SCHWEINHART L.J. & WEIKART D.P. (1980) *Young Children Grow Up: The Effects of the Perry Preschool Program on Youths Through Age 15*. Monographs of the High Scope Educational Research Foundation No. 7. Ypsilanti, Mich: The High Scope Press.

SCROGGS C.L. (1983) 'An examination of the communication interactions between hearing impaired infants and their parents'. In Kyle and Woll (1983).

SEARS R.R., MACCOBY E. & LEVIN H. (1957) *Patterns of Child Rearing*. Evanston, Ill: Row, Peterson.

SELMAN R. (1976) 'Toward a structural analysis of developing interpersonal relations concepts: research with normal and disturbed preadolescent boys'. In A.D. Pick (ed.) *Minnesota Symposium on Child Psychology* (Vol. 10). Minneapolis, Minn: University of Minnesota Press.

SHAVELSON R.J. & BOLUS R. (1982) 'Self concept: the interplay of theory and methods'. *Journal of Educational Psychology*, Vol. 74, pp.3–17.

SHEAVYN E.M. (1976) Ch.18, pp.119–22. In RNID (1976).

SHERIDEN M.D. (1968) *The Developmental Progress of Infants and Young Children*. (2nd edn) London: HMSO. (1st published 1960.)

SHERIDEN M.D. (1988) *From Birth to 5 Years: Children's Developmental Progress*. NFER-Nelson Publishing. (1st published 1973.)

SHERIDEN M. D. & PECKHAM C.S. (1975) 'Follow up at 11 years of children who had marked speech defects at 7 years'. *Child: Care, Health and Development*, Vol. 1, No. 1, pp.1–157.

SHEWAN C.M., WISNIEWSKI A.T. & HYMAN C.S. (1987) 'Disentangling incidence and prevalence'. *American Speech and Hearing Association*, Vol. 27, March, p.51. USA Research Division. Rockville: ASHA.

SHIPMAN M.D. (1972) *Childhood: A Sociological Perspective*. NFER Publishing.

SILVERMAN-DRESNER T. & GUILFOYLE G.R. (1972) *Vocabulary Norms for Deaf Children*. Washington DC: A.G. Bell Association.

SKINNER B.F. (1953) *Science and Human Behaviour*. New York: Macmillan.

SKINNER B.F. (1957) *Verbal Behaviour.* Appleton-Century-Crofts.

SKINNER B.F. (1974) *Beyond Freedom and Dignity.* Harmondsworth: Penguin.

SMITH P.K. & COWIE H. (1988) *Understanding Children's Development.* Oxford: Basil Blackwell.

SNOW C.E. (1972) 'Mothers' speech to children learning language'. *Child Development*, Vol. 43, No. 3, pp.549–65.

SNOW C.E. (1979) 'Conversations with children'. In P. Fletcher and M. Garman (eds) *Language Acquisition.* Cambridge University Press.

SNOW C.N. (1977) 'The development of conversation between mothers and babies'. In V. Lee (ed.) *Language Development.* Croom Helm/Open University Press.

SNYDER M. and ICKES W. (1985) 'Personality and social behaviour'. In G. Lindzey and E. Aronson (eds) *The Handbook of Social Psychology (Vol. 2).* (3rd edn) New York: Random House. (1st published 1954.)

SPENCE S.H. (1987) 'The relationship between social-cognitive skills and peer sociometric status'. *British Journal of Developmental Psychology*, Vol. 5, pp.347–56.

SPITZ R. (1945) 'Hospitalism: an enquiry into the genesis of psychiatric conditions in early childhood'. *The Psychoanalytic Study of the Child, Vol. 1.* New York: International Universities Press.

SPITZ R. (1946) 'Hospitalism: a follow-up report'. *The Psychoanalytic Study of the Child, Vol. 2.* New York: International Universities Press.

SPITZ R. (1965) *The First Year of Life.* New York: International Universities Press/W. Godfrey Cobliner.

SPROTT W.J.H. (1958) *Human Groups.* Harmondsworth: Penguin.

STEPHENS M. (1976) *Linguistic Minorities in Western Europe.* Gomer Press.

STERN D. (1977) *The First Relationship: Infant and Mother.* Cambridge, Mass: Harvard University Press.

STERN D.N., SPIEKER S., BARNETT R.K. & MACKAIN K. (1983) 'The prosody of maternal speech: infant age and context related changes', *Journal of Child Language*, Vol. 10, No. 1, pp.1–15.

STERN D.N., SPIEKER S. & MACKAIN K. (1982) 'Intonation contours as signals in maternal speech to prelinguistic infants'. *Developmental Psychology*, Vol. 18, pp.727–35.

STEWART D.A. (1984) 'Mainstreaming deaf children: a different perspective'. *The Journal of the Association of Canadian Educators of the Hearing Impaired*, Vol. 10, No. 2, pp.91–104.

STEWART J.C. (1978) *Counselling Parents of Exceptional Children.* Columbus, Ohio: Charles E. Merrill.

STOEL-GAMMON C. & OTOMO K. (1986) 'Babbling development of hearing-impaired and normally hearing subjects'. *Journal of Speech and Hearing Disorders*, Vol. 51, No. 1, pp.33–41.

STOKOE W.C. (1978) *Sign Language Structure: The First Linguistic Analysis of American Sign Language.* Silver Springs, Md: Linstok Press. (Originally published as G.L. Trager (ed.) *Occasional Papers 8 in Studies in Linguistics.* University of Buffalo, 1960.)

STOKOE W.C. & BATTISON R.M. (1981) 'Sign language, mental health and satisfactory interaction', pp.179–94. In L.M. Stein, E.D. Mindel and T. Jabaley (eds) *Deafness and Mental Health.* New York: Grune & Stratton.

STRACHAN D.P., JARVIS M.J. & SEYERBEND C. (1989) 'Passive smoking, salivary cotinine concentrations and middle ear effusion in seven year old children'. *British Medical Journal*, Vol. 298, No. 6687, pp.1549–52.

STUBBS M. (1979) *Language Schools and Classrooms.* Methuen. (1st published 1976.)

SWISHER M.V. (1992) 'The role of parents in developing visual turn taking in their young deaf children'. *American Annals of the Deaf*, Vol. 137, No. 2, pp.92–100.

SWISHER M.V. & THOMPSON M. (1985) 'Mothers learning simultaneous communication: the dimensions of the task'. *American Annals of the Deaf*, Vol. 130, No. 3, pp.212–17.

SZASZ T.S. (1972) *The Myth of Mental Illness: Foundations of a Theory of Personal Conduct.* London: Paladin. (1st published 1961.)

TAIT M. (1987) 'Making and monitoring progress in the pre-school years'. *Journal of the British Association of Teachers of the Deaf*, Vol. 11, No. 5, pp.143–53.

TAYLOR I.G. (1979) 'The deaf child'. In J. Ballantyne and J. Groves (eds) *Scott-Brown's Diseases of the Ear, Nose and Throat: The Ear.* (4th edn) Butterworth. (1st published 1952.)

TAYLOR I.G. (1985) 'Hearing-impaired babies and methods of communication'. *Ear and Hearing*, Vol. 6, No. 1, pp.25–8.

TERWILLIGER R.F. (1968) *Meaning and Mind: A Study in the Psychology of Language.* Oxford University Press.

THOMAS D. (1985) 'The determinants of teachers' attitudes to integrating the intellectually handicapped'. *British Journal of Educational Psychology*, Vol. 55, pp.251–63.

THOMPSON B. (1974) 'Self-concepts among secondary school pupils'. *Education Research*, Vol. 17, pp.41–7.

TICE D.M. (1991) 'Esteem protection or enhancement? Self handicapping motives and attributions differ by trait self-esteem'. *Journal of Personality and Social Psychology*, Vol. 60, No. 5, pp.711–25.

TIFFEN K. (1986) 'Responsiveness of isolated versus rejected children to social skills training'. *Journal of Child Psychology and Psychiatry*, Vol. 27, No. 3 , pp.343–55.

TOGONU-BICKERSTETH F. & ODEBIYI A.I. (1985) 'Influence of Yoruba beliefs about abnormality on the socialization of deaf children: a research note'. *Journal of Child Psychology and Psychiatry*, Vol. 26, No. 4, pp.639–52.

TREVARTHEN C. (1974) 'Developmental psychology forum: conversations with a two month old'. *New Scientist*, Vol. 62, No. 896, pp.230–5.

TRONICK E., ALS H. & ADAMSON L. (1979) 'Structure of early face to face communication interactions'. In M. Bullowa (ed.) *Before Speech: The Beginning of Interpersonal Communication.* Cambridge University Press.

TRUDGILL P. (1981) *Sociolinguistics: An Introduction.* Harmondsworth: Penguin. (1st published 1974.)

TUCKER I. & NOLAN M. (1984) *Educational Audiology.* Beckenham: Croom Helm.

TUMIM S. (1975) 'Past, present and future'. *Talk*, Vol. 73.

TUMIN W. (1978) 'Parents' views'. *Education Today*, June.

TWEEDIE J. (1987) *Children's Hearing Problems: Their Significance, Detection and Management.* Bristol: Wright.

Van UDEN A.M.J. (1981) 'Early diagnosis of those multiple handicaps in prelingually profoundly deaf children which endanger an education according to the purely oral way'. *Journal of the British Association of Teachers of the Deaf*, Vol. 5, No. 4, pp.112–25.

VANDELL D.L., ANDERSON L.D., EHRHARDT G. & WILSON K.S. (1982) 'Integrating hearing and deaf preschoolers: an attempt to enhance hearing children's interactions with deaf peers'. *Child Development*, Vol. 53, No. 5, pp. 354–63.

VANDELL D.L. & GEORGE L.B. (1981) 'Social interaction in hearing and deaf preschoolers: successes and failures in initiations'. *Child Development*, Vol. 52, No. 2, pp.627–35.

VANDELL D.L. & WILSON K.S. (1987) 'Infants' interactions with mother, sibling and peer: contrasts and relations between interaction systems'. *Child Development,* Vol. 52, No. 1, pp.176–86.

VERNON M. (1968) 'Fifty years of research on the intelligence of the deaf and hard of hearing: a survey of the literature and discussion of implications'. *Journal of Rehabilitation of the Deaf,* Vol. 1, pp.1–11.

VERNON M. (1969) 'Sociological and psychological factors associated with hearing loss'. *Journal of Speech and Hearing Research,* Vol. 12, No. 3, pp.541–63.

VERNON M. (1972) 'Mind over mouth: a rationale for "Total Communication"'. *Volta Review,* Vol. 74, No. 7, p.529.

VERNON M. (1976) 'Communication and the education of deaf and hard of hearing children'. In RNID (1976).

VERNON M. (1981) 'Public law and private distress'. In Montgomery (1981a).

VOELTZ L.M. (1980) 'Children's attitudes towards handicapped peers'. *American Journal of Mental Deficiency,* Vol. 84, No. 5, pp.455–64.

VOLTERRA V. (1981) 'Gestures, signs and words at two years: when does communication become language?'. *Sign Language Studies,* Vol. 33, pp.351–62.

VOLTERRA V. & CASELLI M.C. (1985) 'From gestures and vocalisations to signs and words'. In W. Stokoe and V. Volterra (eds) *Sign Language Research 83.* Silver Spring, Md: Linstok Press.

VYGOTSKY L.S. (1966) *Thought and Language,* Boston: The MIT Press.

VYGOTSKY L.S. (1978) In M. Cole, V. John-Steiner, S. Scribner & E. Souberman (eds) *Mind in Society: The Development of Higher Psychological Processes.* Harvard University Press.

WAGNER H.M. (ed.) (1975) *Alfred Schutz on Phenomenology and Social Relations.* Chicago: The University of Chicago Press. (1st published 1970.)

WALLANDER J.L. (1988) 'The relationship between attention problems in childhood and antisocial behaviour eight years later'. *Journal of Child Psychology and Psychiatry,* Vol. 29, No.1, pp.53–61.

WARD J. & CENTER Y. (1987) 'Attitudes to the integration of disabled children into regular classes: a factor analysis of functional characteristics'. *British Journal of Educational Psychology,* Vol. 57, pp.221–4.

THE WARNOCK REPORT (1978) *Special Educational Needs. Report on the Committee of Enquiry into the Education of Handicapped Children and Young People.* London: HMSO.

WATSON B.U., SULLIVAN P.M., MOELLER M.P. & JENSON J.K. (1982) 'Nonverbal intelligence and English language ability in death children'. *Journal of Speech and Hearing Disorders,* Vol. 47, No. 2, pp.199–204.

WATSON J.B. (1913) 'Psychology as a behaviourist views it'. *Psychological Review,* Vol. 20, pp.158–77.

WATSON T.J. (1976) Ch.1, pp.3–8. In RNID (1976).

WATTS A.F. (1967) *The Language and Mental Development of Children.* Harrap. (1st published 1944.)

WEBER M. (1922a) *Wirtschaft und Gesellschaft.* Tübingen: JCB Mohr. (English translation by A.M. Henderson and T. Parsons (1957) *The Theory of Social and Economic Organization.* Glencoe, Ill: The Free Press.)

WEBER M. (1922b) *Gesammelte Aufsätze zur Wissenschaftslehere.* Tübingen: J.C.B. Mohr. (A partial translation of this work in E.A. Shils and H.A. Finch (eds) (1949) *Max Weber on the Methodology of the Social Sciences.* Glencoe, Ill: The Free Press.)

WEBSTER A., SCANLON P. & BOWN E. (1985) 'Meeting the needs of hearing-impaired children within a local education authority'. *Journal of the Association of*

Educational Psychologists, Supplement to Vol. 6, No. 5, pp.2–10.

WEBSTER A. & WOOD D. (1989) *Children with Hearing Difficulties.* Cassell Educational.

WEBSTER E.J. (1976) *Professional Approaches with Parents of Handicapped Children.* Springfield Ill: Charles C. Thomas.

WELLMAN H.M. & ESTES E. (1986) 'Early understanding of mental entities: a re-examination of childhood realism'. *Child Development,* Vol. 57, No. 4, pp.910–23.

WEST J.B. (ed.) (1985) *Best and Taylor's Physiological Basis of Medical Practice.* (11th edn) Williams and Wilkins. (1st published 1937.)

WHARRAD H.J. (1988) 'Neonatal hearing screening tests'. Ch.3, pp.69–95. In McCormick (1988c).

WHITE G. (1977) *Socialisation.* Longman.

WHORF B.L. (1950) 'A linguistic consideration of thinking in primitive communications'. In D. Hymes (ed.) *Language in Culture and Society.* Harper and Row.

WHORF B.L. (1956) *Language, Thought and Reality: Selected Writings of Benjamin Lee Whorf/edited by J.B. Carroll.* Cambridge, Mass: MIT Press.

WILKINSON N. (1979) *Teaching Language to Deaf Children.* Special Education Publications. Unwin Brothers.

WINZER M.A. (1982) 'An examination of some selected factors that affected the education and socialization of the deaf of Ontario, 1870–1900'. *Dissertation Abstracts International,* Vol. 43, No. 3, pp.761–2.

WITTGENSTEIN L. (1953) *Philosophical Investigations.* (Translated from the German by G.E.M. Anscombe.) Oxford: Basil Blackwell.

WOLFF J.G. (1976) *Language, Brain and Hearing.* Methuen.

WOLL B. (1987) 'Book review'. *Biological Psychology,* Vol. 25, No.3, pp.280–2.

WOLL B., KYLE J. & DEUCHAR M. (1981) *Perspectives on British Sign Language.* Beckenham: Croom Helm.

WOLL B. & LAWSON L. (1981) 'British Sign Language', pp.218–41. In E. Haugen, J.D. McClure and D. Thomson (eds) *Minority Languages Today.* Edinburgh University Press.

WOOD D. (1982) 'Fostering language development in hearing-impaired children'. Paper presented to 5th Priorsfield Symposium, University of Birmingham.

WOOD D., WOOD H., GRIFFITHS A. & HOWARTH I. (1986) *Teaching and Talking with Deaf Children.* John Wiley.

WOOD M. (1987) 'The role of deaf adults in the education of deaf children', pp.38–40. In *Proceedings of a Conference: Educating the Deaf Child, The Bilingual Option, 17 October 1987, Rycote Centre, Derby.* A LASER publication. (Language of Sign as an Educational Resource.)

WOOD M. (1988) 'Why do we need to train and prepare deaf people?', pp.15–17. In *Proceedings of a Conference: Deaf Adults Working in Education, 12 November 1988, College of Further Education, Derby.* A LASER publication. (Language of Sign as an Educational Resource.)

WOOD S. (1988) 'Pure Tone Audiometry', Ch.6, pp.137–66. In McCormick (1988c).

WOODFORD D.E. (1987) 'English: first or second?'. *Journal of the British Association of Teachers of the Deaf ,* Vol. 11, No. 6, pp.167–72.

WOODWARD J. (1980) 'Some sociolinguistic aspects of French and American Sign Language', pp.103–18. In H. Lane and F. Grosjean (eds) *Recent Perspectives on American Sign Language.* Hillside, NJ: Erlbaum.

WOOLLETT A. (1986) 'The influence of older siblings on the language environment of young children'. *British Journal of Developmental Psychology,* Vol. 4, Pt 3, pp.

235–45.

WOOLLEY H., STEIN A., FORREST G.C. & BAUM J.D. (1989) 'Imparting the diagnosis of life threatening illness in children'. *British Medical Journal*, Vol. 298, No. 6688, pp.1623–6.

WORKING PARTY ON SIGNED ENGLISH (undated) *Signed English for Schools, Vol. 1.* (Further information from: Mr David Baker, Research and Information Officer, Working Party on Signed English, 20, Magdelene Road, Exeter, Devon, EX2 4TD.)

WRIGHT D. (1969) *Deafness: A Personal Account.* Harmondsworth: Allen Lane.

WRIGHT D. (1987) *Scott Brown's Otolaryngology: Basic Sciences.* (5th edn) Butterworth International Edition.

YOUNGER A.J. & BOKYO K.A. (1987) 'Aggression and withdrawal as social schemes underlying children's peer perception'. *Child Development*, Vol. 58, No. 4, pp.1094–100.

ZIGLER E.F. & CHILD I.L. (1973) *Socialization and Personality Development.* Reading, Mass: Addison-Wesley.

ZIMBARD P. & EBBESEN E. (1970) *Influencing Attitudes and Changing Behaviours.* Reading, Mass: Addison-Wesley. (1st published 1969.)

Index

207